Dec Cont
T3-ANT-652

ACKNOWLEDGMENTS

The Publisher would like to thank the following for their help and advice: Brian & Sheena Butler, Jill Douglas, James Burnett, Douglas Clisby, Peter Paige, Patsy Staggs, Laurie Cooper, and the British Hallmarking Council.

DESIGN & TYPESETTING

by

Typography/Graphics, Cathedral City, California 92234

ANTIQUES — A BUYERS' GUIDE TO LONDON

Is published annually by Paige Publications, P.O. Box 1384, Rancho Mirage, California 92270. *Every effort has been made throughout this guide to ensure that the information given is accurate. Although the publishers would be grateful to learn of errors, they can not accept any liability for any loss or expense caused by any errors or omissions which may have occurred.* *No portion of this publication may be reproduced without the express written permission of the Publisher.* *The Publisher reserves the right to reject any editorial or advertising material.*

Copyright © Paige Publications 1987.

ISBN 0-938699-01-6

Antiques –
a buyers' guide to
London

Front Cover

An early Victorian presentation snuffbox.
Elkington & Co. Birmingham 1848.
(Illustrated London News)

CONTENTS

From the Publisher

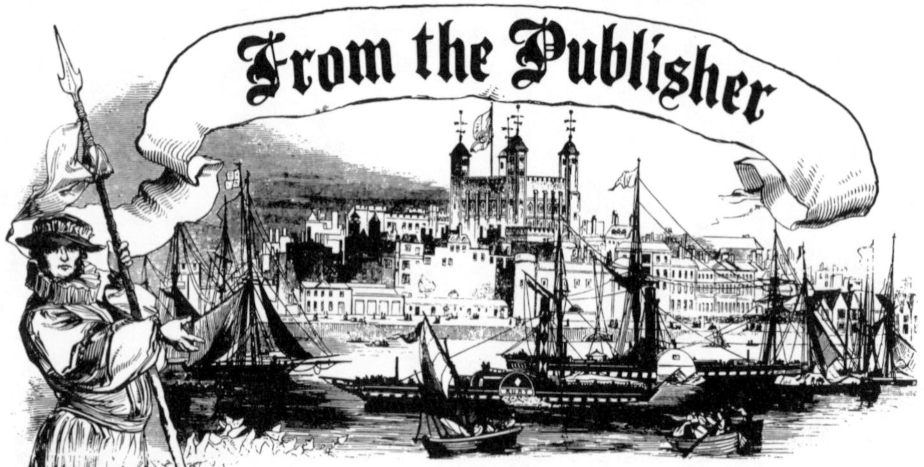

London consists of the largest collection of villages in the world. It is a conglomerate of communities joined by a totally unplanned road system and an abundance of one-way streets which can frustrate even a resident Londoner. However, it is still one of the most exciting cities in the world, and fortunately, getting around in this great metropolis is not difficult. It is better served by its public transport than most other large cities, therefore, I personally would not recommend driving in town. Apart from having to drive on the 'wrong' side of the road, parking is extremely difficult in central London. London Transport's network of buses and underground trains covers the city efficiently and, in the case of the underground, is the fastest way to get around. I have included a map of the underground in the rear of this edition.

This year Caroline Penman, in addition to her Chelsea and West London Fairs, has planned a fair in the Barbican Centre in the City of London. This will be the first such fair to be held in the City but, with Caroline's expertise in this field, I am certain it will become as popular as her other fairs. The fair takes place on November 24-28 — just in time for Christmas shopping! The City is not exactly over-endowed with antique shops but, anyone with an interest in the history of London, will find that any time spent in this area will be time well-spent. It is the oldest part of this capital city and has its own Mayor and police force. One of my favorite places to visit is the Museum of London at 150 London Wall, near the Barbican. The Museum comprises collections relating to the history of London from the Stone Age period to the 20th Century. The Lord Mayor's Ceremonial Coach is on display here — except when in use during the Lord Mayor's Show in early-November. The Museum recently relocated and combined with The Guildhall Museum to display rich theatrical and costume collections, antiquities, armour, paintings and an impressive model of St. Paul's Cathedral before the Great Fire of London in 1666. The Museum is open Tuesday-Saturday 10.00-6.00 and Sunday 2.00-6.00. The City of London covers no more than one square mile yet, for the history buff's amongst you, a visit to the "Wall Street" of Britain is not to be missed.

For those of you who may like to venture to the Continent, the third Antiquairs International & Pictura Fine Art Fair will take place from 7th-15th March in the Eurohal of the Maastricht Conference Centre in The Nederlands. The Centre is conveniently situated near the airport — ideal for those making a day trip from London. This prestigious event offers a marvelous opportunity for dealers and collectors to meet leading international dealers under one roof. American dealers, Chevalier Inc. of New York and Brian Michael Powers Inc. of California, will join other major dealers from Belgium, France, Germany, Italy, The Nederlands, Switzerland and the United Kingdom. Maastricht is the oldest city in The Nederlands and has a wealth of historic buildings, monuments and museums. For further information, contact Sue Bond, 46 Greswell Street, London SW6 6PP. Tel: 01 381 1324.

Some of you may feel that you need assistance on your buying trips. Well, the Harwoods have the answer. Diane and Peter Harwood, proprietors of the Antique Village Antiques Mall in Laguna Hills, California, offer personally escorted tours of Britain and Europe for antique dealers and collectors. Diane and Peter, now U.S. citizens, were born in Chester, England and, having imported fine antiques themselves for many years, they are in an excellent position to introduce you to many major antique wholesalers. Their itinerary is very flexible, giving their small groups of 14-16 guests the freedom to pursue their personal interests whether it be shopping, sightseeing, golfing or of course antiqueing. They arrange for the collection, packing and shipping of your purchases back to the U.S.A. at great savings. This year they are also introducing a 'Business Trip' for the antique dealer or collector on a tight schedule. They anticipate a very busy year ahead, so it is wise to contact them at an early date. To receive a tour brochure, contact Diane or Peter at (714) 951 9051.

For those of you on an even tighter schedule, in fact unable to make the trip at all, Victory Finders in London will help you find that special item or items you are looking for. They offer an extensive buying service using highly reputable dealers in England and France and will send details and color photographs by express mail for you to examine. They also provide an experienced courier service and assistance in arranging hotel accomodation. I feel they are providing a much needed service and, with their expertise, could save the American buyer a great deal of time and trouble. For further information, contact Mr. K. Fry, London House, 271-273 King Street, London W6 9LZ. Tel: 01 741 8011.

Although, when I started this project, I knew there was a need for this type of guide in the U.S., I did not realize just how much demand there would be. This is my second edition and, after a shaky start last year (due mainly to the terrorism influence on the travel scene) sales picked up tremendously in September/October and are still going strong. I am very encouraged by the response and fully intend to update and publish this guide on an annual basis. It is designed to assist you in your search for antiques and I do hope that you will find it useful in the planning stages of your trip and for reference during your stay in London. If I can be of any further assistance to you, please don't hesitate to write to me.

Irene Paige, Publisher

LUXURY TRAVEL FOR THE DISCRIMINATING INDIVIDUAL

STOPOVERS OF 2, 3, & EVEN 4 NIGHTS AT MOST HOTELS

NEW FOR 1987 SPECIAL ANTIQUE DEALERS "BUSINESS TRIP"

Low Cost • Intensive Buying • Short Stay

ANTIQUE COLLECTING & SIGHTSEEING TOURS OF EUROPE & BRITAIN

MAY & SEPTEMBER 1987

DELUXE TOUR of BRITAIN & EUROPE

Exclusive Features That Give You Unbeatable Value For Money:

- Small, intimate groups of only 14 to 16 guests.
- All tours personally escorted by Diane and Peter Harwood, Antique Dealers.
- A luxury full length executive motorcoach especially fitted with tables, wet bar, toilet, etc.
- Full "A La Carte" breakfasts and dinners served per itinerary.
- Stays of two, three and 4 nights in world famous country inns and elegant hotels.
- A pace that really lets you enjoy Europe's people, countryside and wealth in antiques.
- A complete service for collecting, packing and shipping your purchases back to the USA.
- The daily freedom to go sightseeing antiqueing, golfing, etc. whichever you choose.
- This tour can be 100 percent tax deductible. (Check with your CPA)
- May 1987 departure.

Send For Brochure

PLUS

A Complete & Inexpensive Service For Collecting, Packing & Shipping Your Purchases

ANTIQUE BUYING "BUSINESS TRIP"

September 1987 Departure

11 DAYS IN BRITAIN

$1180.00*

Land Cost Only

HERITAGE

Village Tours Intl.

23200 Del Lago, Laguna Hills, CA 92653

(714) 951-9051

ASTA

EARLY PINE FURNITURE

Downstairs has now moved Upstairs

By Jill Douglas

A hush fell over the auction room as Lot 349 soared above the £3,000 mark. It had been listed in the catalog as "A pair of 19th Century pine cabinets, each with dentil cornice, single barred glazed door enclosing adjustable shelves, 2 panelled doors below Greek key pattern bands; width 34 in., height 86 in." Most of the dealers had put a price of £1,500 on this lot, but here it was doubling their estimates. The auctioneer's hammer finally fell at £3,400 ($5,100). Stripped pine had shown itself able to command top price, a price exceeding that of many other woods. Where had it been for the last century, and why is it so sought-after?

Georgian corner cupboard, c. 1820, formerly built in. New back added to make it free-standing.

After remaining so long in obscurity, in most cases covered with layers of paint, pine has come into its own as a result of a growing demand that began about twenty-five years ago: part of a "back to basics" trend emphasizing the use of natural materials in interior decoration, natural clothing fabrics and natural foods. In England, this trend in home furnishings was popularized by designers such as Laura Ashley and Terence Conran, amongst others. In California, as in many parts of America, pine is a part of our pioneer heritage, and in today's high-tech world it answers our need to keep in touch with an earlier, more simple life-style. Part of its appeal is its versatility: you can strip it or paint it, you can even remove the doors of a cupboard to reveal the shelves inside, and provided that this is tastefully done the value of the piece will be unaffected.

English and Irish pine dating prior to the 19th Century is rare. Early English furniture was made of the wood most commonly found in England's forests, namely oak, and this wood was used in town and country until the introduction of walnut furniture from Holland in the mid-17th Century. With walnut, and later, mahogany, came the art of veneering (not for the purpose of deception, but to produce an effect that was more beautiful because of a greater choice of wood patterns and grains). Oak as a base for veneering was unsatisfactory, the veneer having a tendency to come away from it, and so pine (or deal, as it was sometimes called) was often used instead. Today it is possible to find beautifully made chests-of-drawers and other cabinet-work in pine showing a craftsmanship greater than that of the country carpenter, and in some cases this is because the pieces were originally veneered; with the veneer removed, the basic pine article is revealed. Antique pine of superior quality can be found for other reasons, one being that most alcove cupboards were made in pine since they were generally built in with the panelling and painted the same color. Eighteenth Century corner cupboards and niches with their arched cornices, fielded panel doors and side moldings can rival any furniture in any wood. Pine is easier to carve than hardwood and there are examples of carving on early pine console tables, stools, wall brackets and the like, originally gilded. For reasons of economy, some of the classical painted furniture of the early 19th Century was made of pine, including the "faux bamboo" designs so popular in Regency England. And we must not forget that although the market for top quality furniture in mahogany and other expensive woods was relatively small, there was a steady demand for well-made but less expensive pieces, usually in pine, stained or painted to resemble the darker woods. These would have been made by provincial cabinet-makers who by the late 18th Century had advanced in skill, some of them making excellent copies of the patterns of Chippendale, such as they might have seen in the pages of "The Director".

Today, however, pine is invariably associated with the simple country furniture for which it was mostly used. It was plentiful, it was easy to work and it was inexpensive, and by the 19th Century it had replaced oak as the primary wood used in England's rural areas. However, pine was too soft for the wear demanded of chairs; beech, elm and ash were generally used for this purpose. The village carpenter or joiner made much of the cottage furniture, sometimes it would even be home-made. The designs were simple, but there were regional variations and developments, such as Welsh dressers, Lancashire settles, and "cricket" tables from the south-eastern counties near London. Ireland's country furniture tradition was established after the famine and emigration of the mid-19th Century, when economic improvements combined with a ready supply of good imported pine and the availability of skilled craftsmen working in the countryside. Designs were based on the classical furniture seen on the country estates of the Anglo-Irish gentry (where many of the craftsmen were employed), but inventive and imaginative interpretations gave Irish country furniture its special character. It was painted to protect the timber from the damp conditions as well as to enrich its appearance, and the colors were bright and varied.

An interesting example of Irish design is the pine trunk or blanket chest, although what we call blanket chests were in fact multi-purpose. In addition to the storage space, the interior was frequently fitted with a compartment for important documents, and

Late 18th Century breakfront bookcase stripped of its mahogany veneer. The interior was originally painted.

concealed drawers for money and small valuables. The lid often sloped and could serve as a writing surface for household or farm accounts which would then be stored in the chest. Removal of the paint reveals fine joinery and dovetailing, and sometimes the skillful use of molding to conceal joins and add interest.

Throughout Queen Victoria's reign and well into the Edwardian era, pine furniture was being mass-produced in England's industrial areas; many pieces were made by noted furniture makers such as Liberty's and Maples, but most of it was of an inferior quality and was bought by those of modest means or by the owners of larger homes for use in the servants' quarters. Since pine was a cheap wood, people who could only afford pine naturally wanted to hide the fact and so it was painted or stained to resemble the more aristocratic woods. Bedroom items such as chests-of-drawers, wash-stands and wardrobes were generally painted white in keeping with the Victorians' moral emphasis on cleanliness. Inexpensive woods needed to be sealed, too, and so painting served a double purpose — perhaps we could say a triple purpose since the layers of paint have helped to protect it for us until now. Even these poorer quality, mass-produced items are in demand today; they are so simply made that restoration is not a problem.

Perhaps the most familiar item of early pine furniture is the Welsh dresser. The traditional dresser, with its superstructure of shelves above a cupboard, evolved in 17th Century Wales from the early oak dresser-table. The shelves above the table grew in number and were eventually enclosed in a frame, then came cupboards and drawers, some above the table top, others below. There was no set pattern, although three drawers below was a common feature, the smaller central drawer being used for knives. By the 19th Century the pine dresser was so integral a part of "downstairs" life in the larger homes that it was usually built into the kitchen wall. In Ireland the dresser made its appearance in the late 18th Century, not of oak, as was general in England at that time, but of imported pine, the only timber available in quantity. During the 19th Century it was rapidly adopted by the Irish and underwent a number of modifications. The upper portion was decorated with fretwork, columns, applied molding and a wide variety of decorative motifs, many of them related to Celtic design; ornamentation to the base was usually confined to the panelled doors. Some bases incorporated a hen-coop, single or double-tiered. Irish dressers were always painted, sometimes in bright contrasting colors but more frequently in imitation of mahogany.

19th Century Irish dresser incorporating a hen-coop in the base.

The large pine table so much in demand today was originally made as a work table for the cook, but it doubled as a dining table for servants; on the farm it was used for the communal meals of family, domestic servants and farm workers who would take their meals in the farmhouse kitchen. These tables had a wide apron, necessary for overall strength, deep drawers for utensils, and solid square legs connected by a stout stretcher. One clue to a table's age can be detected from its legs. Flagstone floors were damp from regular washing as well as from weather conditions, causing wood to rot. The rotted wood was sawn off — sometimes replaced, sometimes not — which accounts for some of the older tables being lower than normal table height. Irish pine tables were similar to those found all over Britain, however smaller tables from post-famine Ireland were often made with a double stretcher which was used as a pot-ledge.

Desks are common in pine, mostly Victorian kneehole desks. Highbacked settles are another popular item; known as "screens" in the Welsh border counties, they can still be seen in old pubs screening off the fire and allowing a passage-way behind them. The variety of early pine is extensive and includes domestic items, boxes of all sorts and sizes, picture and mirror frames, cradles, commodes and clock-cases, as well as the larger pieces already discussed. However, a word about dating antique pine. First, it is far more difficult to date period pine than other woods as all of the original paint has usually been removed. To say that a date can be established by the way a piece has been constructed is not infallible, as any present-day craftsman can prove. On the other hand, it is far easier to spot reconstruction and "marriages" as there is little camouflage from coloring.

19th Century Irish fiddle-front dresser base, now used as a buffet.

We have been asked many times about the best way to preserve stripped pine. On our last visit to England we made the rounds of strippers and dealers to find out what they did, and almost invariably they were using **Bri-wax** or a similar product such as **Black Bison.** In olden times pine tables, and sometimes other pine pieces, were scrubbed with soap and water, but this eventually matts the wood fibers and gives a woolly look. This cannot occur if you apply wax with fine steel wool, then burnish with a brush and finally shine with a soft cloth.

This books lists many sellers of pine, but as you travel the by-roads of England you will occasionally chance upon a stripper at work. These places can sometimes be sources of fine pine that is a little cheaper than the London market. There is the fascinating shop converted from an old church in the town of Lewes, in Sussex, which Mary Sautter has turned into a wonderland of pine. If you go there, remember that the smaller, cheaper items are upstairs in the choir-loft. In the nearby town of Worthing, former California resident Mike Barratt runs The Antique Workshop; he has a good selection of pine at reasonable prices, and strips on the premises.

If imitation is the sincerest form of flattery, then the amount of reproduction pine now being made would indicate that the poor relation, hiding for so long behind paint and veneer, has come into its own at last. Quality stripped pine can be recognized as superb furniture in its own right, and hand-crafted cottage and country pine is no less desirable. Oak, walnut and mahogany are rich-looking and elegant, but pine has a charm that is unique. It is simple, unpretentious, easy to care for and has a warm and cheerful look. In short, it is comfortable to live with; and the more technically complex our world becomes, the more we shall instinctively turn to Nature for our home environment. For these reasons alone, pine is likely to be with us for many generations to come.

Jill Douglas is the owner of Mark Douglas Antiques (importers of English furniture and china), 291 26th Street, Santa Monica, California 90402. Tel: (213) 395-8914.

Choose Europe's Choice

Briwax, the preferred wax/reconditioner in Europe for well over a century, is fast becoming America's favorite. International success is proof of Briwax's ability to remove water marks, scratches, and grease while it reconditions all your household furnishings. One step does it all, simply apply and rub lightly. Available in 4 shades. Your possessions will be beautiful tomorrow.

BRIWAX Does It . . . Naturally.

BRIWAX

BRIWAX INTERNATIONAL
P.O. Box 3327, Redwood City, CA 94064
(415) 369-3711 / Toll Free (800) 227-9744

The Chelsea Antiques Fair

Famous since 1951 – Twice a year, on King's Road, London S.W.3.

10 - 21 March 1987

8 - 19 September 1987

A carefully balanced selection of top English Dealers – (most B.A.D.A. members) offer their finest wares. Almost all pre 1830.

Adm: £2.50 incl, catalogue
Group rate on application

Shipping agent in attendance

Enquiries:
Penman Fairs, P.O. Box 114
Haywards Heath, W. Sussex
Telephone 04447–2514

Victory Finders

LONDON ● PARIS

- offers the American Antique buyer an extensive and personalised search and buying service in England and France.
- available to the trade and private individuals.
- eliminates the time and expense of personal trips.
- highly reputable English and French dealers used.
- full details and colour photographs sent by express airmail prior to agreement to purchase.
- experienced and friendly courier service available, and hotel or apartment accommodation arranged for personal visitors to England or France.

For further information please contact:

Mr K. N. Fry
London House
271-273 King Street
London W6 9LZ
England
Tel: (England) 01-741 8011

THE LEGACY OF SPODE

Although English pottery did not achieve any importance until the eighteenth century, England can congratulate itself on possessing a race of potters unsurpassed in the world. This is largely due to the craft having its chief center in one district — the Staffordshire Potteries — where generations have learned the art from father to son, and thus carried on the traditions of their founders.

Josiah Spode

Josiah Spode's name springs to fame in 1770 when, having successfully mastered the art of pottery making at Thomas Whieldon's pottery, "Old Spode" as he was often called, founded his factory at Stoke-on-Trent. His work was of the finest quality and in great demand. He perfected the process of transfer printing. This method of printing from copper engravings had already been in use for some fifteen to twenty years, but designs were usually of pastoral scenes and confined to small plates. Spode's creative mind saw wider possibilities and, by a clever adaptation of this process, the world is indebted to him for those exquisite blue printed designs which are so collectable today.

Josiah Spode I was not only an expert potter but a very shrewd business man. He opened a salesroom in London under the management of William Copeland, a London banker who also traded in tea with the Far East. It is a well known fact that only a china teapot can bring out the true flavoring of tea so this was a useful outlet for Spode's wares. William Copeland was also in a position to supply Spode with many Chinese designs through his contracts with the Orient.

Josiah's eldest son, also named Josiah, entered the business and became as famous as his father. Upon his father's death in 1797, Josiah Spode II assumed the management of the factory and, with the co-operation of William Copeland in London, business increased tremendously and Spode chinaware was exported to all parts of the world. Spode had taken William Copeland into partnership and this proved so successful that Copeland brought his only son, also named William, into the business. Their factory became the largest and most affluent one in the Potteries. Even in those days they employed 800 people and the buildings covered over eight acres of ground.

Josiah Spode II must be credited with turning the manufacture of porcelain into a commercial success. Porcelain had been made at Chelsea, Bow and Worcester as early as 1750, but the paste used was of a soft nature which, when fired, was very liable to become distorted. By introducing bone ash into the porcelain, Spode's formula ensured a hard durable, pure white porcelain — this became the standard for English bone china and is still used by most bone china manufacturers.

Spode, however, did not limit himself to the making of porcelain; in 1805 he perfected his "Stone China" — a type of earthenware with a charming greyish tint resembling Chinese porcelain. This "Stone China" was of a harder nature and, with Chinese-style polychrome decoration, it became immensely popular both in England and on the Continent.

William Copeland died in 1826 and his son, William Taylor Copeland, took his place in the firm. Josiah Spode II died in 1827 at the age of 73 and, in 1833, William Taylor Copeland purchased the entire interest from the trustees of Spode and became sole owner of the business. To this second William Copeland we owe one of the most important advances in porcelain-making during the nineteenth century i.e. the production of Parian. Parian is a statuary porcelain somewhat resembling the material which the Derby factory had used for their famous Biscuit figures. The Copeland recipe, while not so waxy-looking, resembled a fine statuary marble. It became very fashionable and enormous quantities of statuettes, busts and ornamental pieces were produced, many from models designed by John Gibson R.A. and J.H Foley R.A. This hard-paste unglazed porcelain, known initially as "statuary porcelain", was given the name Parian as it resembled the famous marble from the Greek Island of Paros.

William Taylor Copeland become Lord Mayor of London in 1835 and took Thomas Garrett, a Staffordshire potter, into partnership. The firm traded as Copeland and Garrett until 1847, when the partnership was dissolved. It then become W.T. Copeland, late Spode until 1867 when it became W.T. Copeland and Sons. In 1970, two hundred years after "Old Spode" founded his factory, the name reverted to Spode. Josiah Spode I's high standards have been upheld over the years and they still aim at producing nothing but the very best in quality, design and color. Pride of workmanship, and the desire to make beautiful specimens of the potter's art inspire the craftsmen today as they did in the days of the Spodes.

ITALIAN

Blue Printed Ware produced by Spode in 1775,
illustrating Roman ruins, and executed by celebrated engravers.

The district known as the "Staffordshire Potteries" or just "The Potteries" comprises a number of towns, the main ones being Burslem, Cobridge, Etruria, Fenton, Hanley, Longton, Stoke-on-Trent and Tunstall. Many of the factories conduct guided tours; they also have their own factory shops (stores) and museum displays. For further information contact Tourist Information Centre, 1 Glebe Street, Stoke-on-Trent, Staffordshire ST4 1HP. Tel: (0782) 411222.

SPODE-COPELAND TRADE MARKS

Used by the firm since its inception, 1770.

Spode

Spode

SPODE

Spode Felspar Porcelain

SPODE
Felspar Porcelain

SPODE
Stone-China

SPODE

Spodes New Fayence

Spode's Imperial

SPODE, SON & COPELAND or SPODE & COPELAND,

COPELAND AND GARRETT

COPELAND & GARRETT

COPELAND & GARRETT NEW FAYENCE

COPELAND & GARRETT LATE SPODE THE TIBER

Copeland Late Spode.

Copeland Late Spode

COPELAND

Copeland Stone China

COPELAND

COPELAND

COPELAND LATE SPODE

SPODE
COPELAND'S CHINA
ENGLAND

COPELAND late SPODE ENGLAND

Spode
Impl

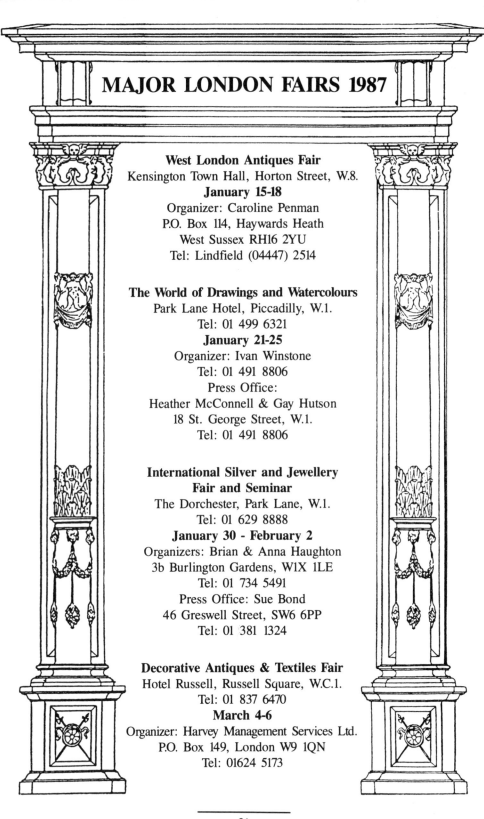

MAJOR LONDON FAIRS 1987

West London Antiques Fair
Kensington Town Hall, Horton Street, W.8.
January 15-18
Organizer: Caroline Penman
P.O. Box 114, Haywards Heath
West Sussex RH16 2YU
Tel: Lindfield (04447) 2514

The World of Drawings and Watercolours
Park Lane Hotel, Piccadilly, W.1.
Tel: 01 499 6321
January 21-25
Organizer: Ivan Winstone
Tel: 01 491 8806
Press Office:
Heather McConnell & Gay Hutson
18 St. George Street, W.1.
Tel: 01 491 8806

International Silver and Jewellery Fair and Seminar
The Dorchester, Park Lane, W.1.
Tel: 01 629 8888
January 30 - February 2
Organizers: Brian & Anna Haughton
3b Burlington Gardens, W1X 1LE
Tel: 01 734 5491
Press Office: Sue Bond
46 Greswell Street, SW6 6PP
Tel: 01 381 1324

Decorative Antiques & Textiles Fair
Hotel Russell, Russell Square, W.C.1.
Tel: 01 837 6470
March 4-6
Organizer: Harvey Management Services Ltd.
P.O. Box 149, London W9 1QN
Tel: 01624 5173

1987 ANTIQUE FAIRS

The Chelsea Antiques Fair

March 10-21
Sept. 8-19

40 stands, highest quality.
strictly vetted, most items pre 1830

Adm: £2.50 incl Catalogue

Chelsea Old Town Hall, Kings Rd, SW3

WEST LONDON Antiques Fair

January 15-18
August 13-16

Kensington Town Hall, Horton St, W8

Adm: £2 incl Catalogue

90 stands, good quality.
Vetted mostly pre 1870

THE CITY OF LONDON ANTIQUES FAIR

NOVEMBER 24~28

The Barbican Exhibition Centre
100 stands, high quality
most items pre-1870

Admission: £2 incl. Catalogue

Brighton Antiques Fair

8-11 July

Corn Exchange,
Royal Pavilion Grounds, Sussex

75 stands, mostly 1870 datelined
Adm: £1.50 incl Catalogue

For further details & group rates:

Caroline Penman
P.O. Box 114
Haywards Heath
W. Sussex
RH162YU

Tel Lindfield
(04447) 2514

Penman Antiques Fairs

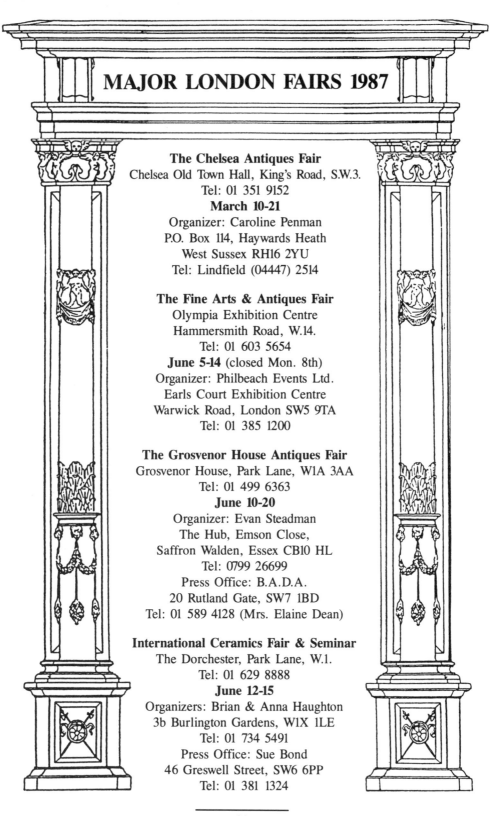

MAJOR LONDON FAIRS 1987

The Chelsea Antiques Fair
Chelsea Old Town Hall, King's Road, S.W.3.
Tel: 01 351 9152
March 10-21
Organizer: Caroline Penman
P.O. Box 114, Haywards Heath
West Sussex RH16 2YU
Tel: Lindfield (04447) 2514

The Fine Arts & Antiques Fair
Olympia Exhibition Centre
Hammersmith Road, W.14.
Tel: 01 603 5654
June 5-14 (closed Mon. 8th)
Organizer: Philbeach Events Ltd.
Earls Court Exhibition Centre
Warwick Road, London SW5 9TA
Tel: 01 385 1200

The Grosvenor House Antiques Fair
Grosvenor House, Park Lane, W1A 3AA
Tel: 01 499 6363
June 10-20
Organizer: Evan Steadman
The Hub, Emson Close,
Saffron Walden, Essex CB10 HL
Tel: 0799 26699
Press Office: B.A.D.A.
20 Rutland Gate, SW7 1BD
Tel: 01 589 4128 (Mrs. Elaine Dean)

International Ceramics Fair & Seminar
The Dorchester, Park Lane, W.1.
Tel: 01 629 8888
June 12-15
Organizers: Brian & Anna Haughton
3b Burlington Gardens, W1X 1LE
Tel: 01 734 5491
Press Office: Sue Bond
46 Greswell Street, SW6 6PP
Tel: 01 381 1324

MAJOR LONDON FAIRS 1987

The Antiquarian Book Fair
The Park Lane Hotel, Piccadilly, W.1.
Tel: 01 499 6321
June 23-25
Organizer:
Antiquarian Booksellers Association
Suite 2, 26 Charing Cross Road, W.C.2.
Tel: 01 379 3041
Press Office: Heather McConnell
18 St. George Street, W.1.
Tel: 01 493 6420

West London Antiques Fair
Kensington Town Hall, Horton Street, W.8.
August 13-16
Organizer: Caroline Penman
P.O. Box 114, Haywards Heath
West Sussex RH16 2YU
Tel: Lindfield (04447) 2514

The Chelsea Antiques Fair
Chelsea Old Town Hall, King's Road, S.W.3.
Tel: 01 351 9152
September 8-19
Organizer: Caroline Penman
P.O. Box 114, Haywards Heath
West Sussex RH16 2YU
Tel: Lindfield (04447) 2514

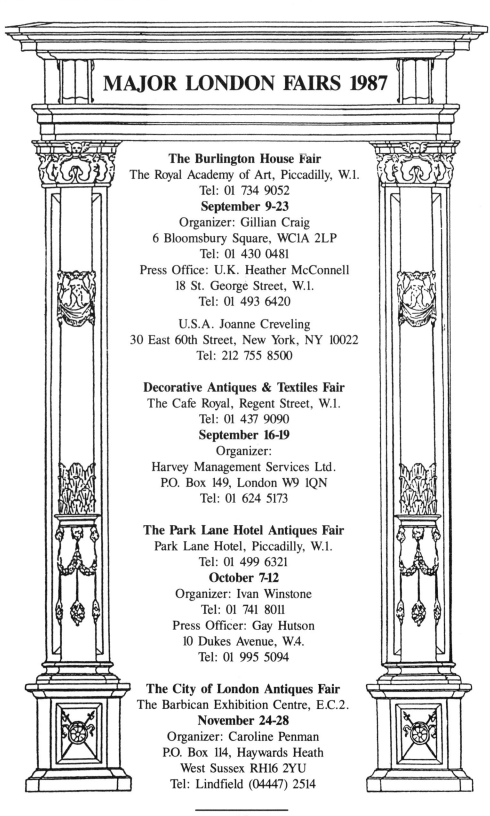

MAJOR LONDON FAIRS 1987

The Burlington House Fair
The Royal Academy of Art, Piccadilly, W.1.
Tel: 01 734 9052
September 9-23
Organizer: Gillian Craig
6 Bloomsbury Square, WC1A 2LP
Tel: 01 430 0481
Press Office: U.K. Heather McConnell
18 St. George Street, W.1.
Tel: 01 493 6420

U.S.A. Joanne Creveling
30 East 60th Street, New York, NY 10022
Tel: 212 755 8500

Decorative Antiques & Textiles Fair
The Cafe Royal, Regent Street, W.1.
Tel: 01 437 9090
September 16-19
Organizer:
Harvey Management Services Ltd.
P.O. Box 149, London W9 1QN
Tel: 01 624 5173

The Park Lane Hotel Antiques Fair
Park Lane Hotel, Piccadilly, W.1.
Tel: 01 499 6321
October 7-12
Organizer: Ivan Winstone
Tel: 01 741 8011
Press Officer: Gay Hutson
10 Dukes Avenue, W.4.
Tel: 01 995 5094

The City of London Antiques Fair
The Barbican Exhibition Centre, E.C.2.
November 24-28
Organizer: Caroline Penman
P.O. Box 114, Haywards Heath
West Sussex RH16 2YU
Tel: Lindfield (04447) 2514

ANTIQUES MARKETS AND CENTERS

Alfies Antique Market
13-25 Church Street
Marylebone, N.W.8.
Tel: 723 6066
150 dealers
Open Tuesday-Saturday 10am-6pm

Antiquarius
135-141 King's Road
Chelsea, S.W.3.
Tel: 351 5353
200 dealers
Open Monday-Saturday 10am-6pm

Bermondsey Antique Hypermarket
Long Lane/Bermondsey Street, S.E.1.
Tel: 937 1572 or 351 5353
Open Monday-Friday

Bermondsey Antique Market
Long Lane/Bermondsey Street, S.E.1.
Tel: 937 1572 or 351 5353
250 dealers
Open Friday 5am-2pm

Bond Street Antique Centre
124 New Bond Street, W.1.
Tel: 351 5353
25 dealers
Open Monday-Friday 10am-5.45pm

Bond Street Silver Galleries
111-112 New Bond Street, W.1.
Tel: 493 6180
15 dealers- mainly trade
Open Monday-Friday 9am-5.30pm

Camden Antiques Trade Market
Camden High Street/Bucks Street
Camden Town, N.W.1.
Tel: 351 5353
100 dealers
Open Thursday 7am-1pm

Camden Passage Antiques Centre
357 Upper Street, Islington, N.1.
Tel: 359 0190
300 dealers
Open Monday-Friday 10.30am-5.30pm
Market days:
Wed. 8am-3pm General antiques
Thurs. 9am-4pm Books
Sat. 9am-5pm General antiques

Chelsea Antique Market
245-253 King's Road
Chelsea, S.W.3.
Tel: 352 5689
50 dealers
Open Monday-Saturday 10am-6pm

Chenil Galleries
181-183 King's Road, Chelsea, S.W.3.
Tel: 351 5353
80 dealers
Open Monday-Saturday 10am-6pm

The Corner Portobello Antiques Supermarket
282-290 Westbourne Grove, W.11.
Tel: 727 2027
150 dealers
Open Friday 12-4pm
Saturday 7am-6pm

ABC
antique centres
London's finest centres and busiest markets

ANTIQUARIUS

135/141 Kings Rd. Chelsea London SW3
Open Monday to Saturday 10am to 6pm

Roger's Antiques Gallery
65 Portobello Road
London W11
Open every Saturday 7am to 5pm

Bermondsey antique market
& Open Friday mornings 5am to 2pm
Antique Hypermarket
Open Monday to Friday
On the corner of
Long Lane and
Bermondsey St.
London SE1

Bond St.
ANTIQUE CENTRE
124 NEW BOND STREET W1

124 New Bond Street
London W1
Open Monday to Friday
10am to 5.45pm
Saturday 10am to 4pm

Camden antique & collectors market
Corner of Camden High St. and
Buck St. **Camden Town NW1**
Open Thursday mornings 7am to 1pm

antique CHENIL GALLERIES centre
181/183 Kings Road Chelsea SW3
Tel: 01 351 5353

181/183 Kings Rd. Chelsea
London SW3
Open Monday to Saturday
10am to 6pm

Cutler Street antique market
Goulston St. (Aldgate end) EC1
for gold, silver, jewellery, gems,
coins and stamps
Open Sunday morning 7am to 2pm

Information from the Press Office 15 Flood Street London SW3 01-351 5353 Telex 894638

Covent Garden Flea Market
Jubilee Market
Covent Garden, W.C.2.
Tel: 836 2139
Open Monday 6am-4pm

Cutler Street Antique Market
Goulston Street, E.1.
Tel: 351 5353 or 937 1572
Open Sunday 7am-2pm

Dixon's Antique Market Centre
471 Upper Richmond Road West
East Sheen, S.W.14.
Tel: 878 6788
24 dealers
Open Thursday-Tuesday
10am-5.30pm

Franklin's Camberwell Antiques Market
161 Camberwell Road, S.E.5.
Tel: 703 8089
Open Tuesday-Saturday 10am-6pm
Sunday 1pm-6pm

Georgian Village
30/31 Islington Green, N.1.
Tel: 226 1571
Open Wednesday 10am-4pm
Saturday 7am-5pm

Grays Antique Market
58 Davies Street, W.1.
Tel: 629 7034
85 dealers
Open Monday-Friday 10am-6pm

Grays Mews
1-7 Davies Mews, W.1.
Tel: 629 7034
80 dealers
Open Monday-Friday 10am-6pm

Greenwich Antiques Market
Greenwich High Road, S.E.10.
Tel: 405 4970
90 dealers
Open Saturday 7.30am-4.30pm
Sunday 7.30am-4.30pm
(Jun-Sep)

Hampstead Antique Emporium
12 Heath Street
Hampstead, N.W.3.
Tel: 794 3297
25 dealers
Open Tuesday-Saturday 10am-6pm

Howe's Antique Market
72/73 Chalk Farm Road
Camden, N.W.1.
Tel: 267 4499
40 dealers
Open Tuesday-Sunday

The London Silver Vaults
53-65 Chancery Lane, W.C.2.
Tel: 242 3844
32 dealers
Open Monday-Friday 9am-5.30pm
Saturday 9am-12.30pm

The Mall Antiques Arcade
359 Upper Street
Islington, N.1.
Tel: 359 0825
35 dealers
Open Tues, Thurs, Fri 10am-5pm
Wednesday 7.30am-5pm
Saturday 9am-6pm

The Northcote Road Antiques Market
155a Northcote Road, S.W.11
23 dealers
Open Sunday

The Old Stables Market
Stanley Sidings
Chalk Farm Road, N.W.1.
Tel: 723 7970
100 dealers
Open Saturday-Sunday 7am-5pm

Portobello Antiques Market
165-169 Portobello Road, W.11.
Tel: 431 2875
200 dealers
Open Saturday 6am-6pm

Riverdale Hall Antique Market
Lewisham Centre
Rennell Street, S.E.13.
Tel: 599 4076
50 dealers
Open Monday 8.30am-4.30pm

Roger's Antique Galleries
65 Portobello Road, W.11.
Tel: 727 1262 or 351 5353
60 dealers
Open Saturday 7am-5pm

Streatham Traders and Shippers Market
United Reform Church Hall, S.W.16.
Tel: 764 3602
50 dealers
Open Thursday 8am-3pm

World Famous Portobello Market
177 Portobello Road & 1-3 Elgin Crescent, W.11.
Tel: 431 2875
200 dealers
Open Friday-Saturday 6am-6pm

The Chelsea Antique Market

London's First Antique Market For Collectors & Dealers

245 / 253 King's Road, London SW3
(opposite Carlyle Square)
Tel. 01-352 5689 / 1720

1 **Alfies**

2 & 3 **Grays**

4 **Bond Street Silver Galleries**

5 **Bond Street Antique Centre**

6 **Chelsea Antique Market**

7 **Chenil Galleries**

8 **Antiquarius**

⊖ **Underground Stations**

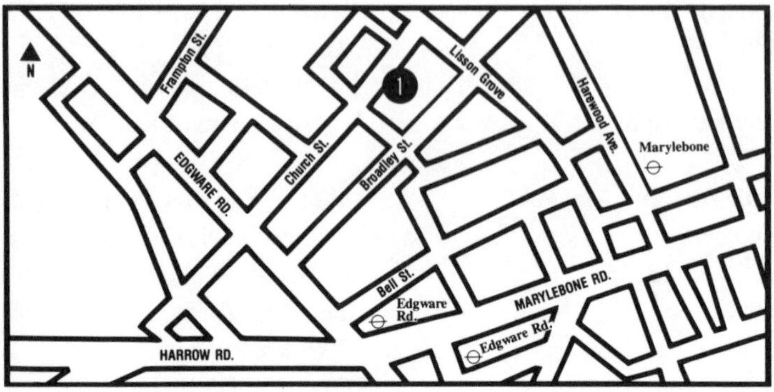

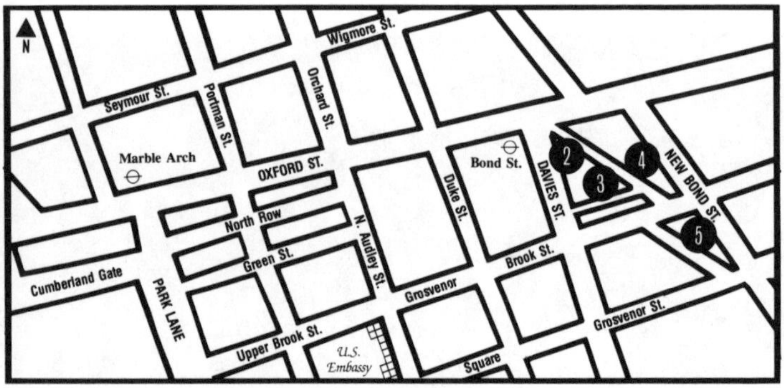

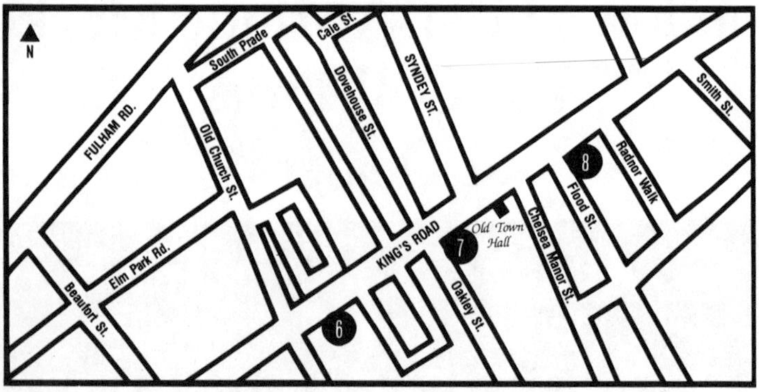

9 **Jubilee Market**

10 **Bermondsey Antique Hyper Market**

11 **Bermondsey Open Antique Market**

12 **Cutler Street Antique Market**

⊖ **Underground Stations**

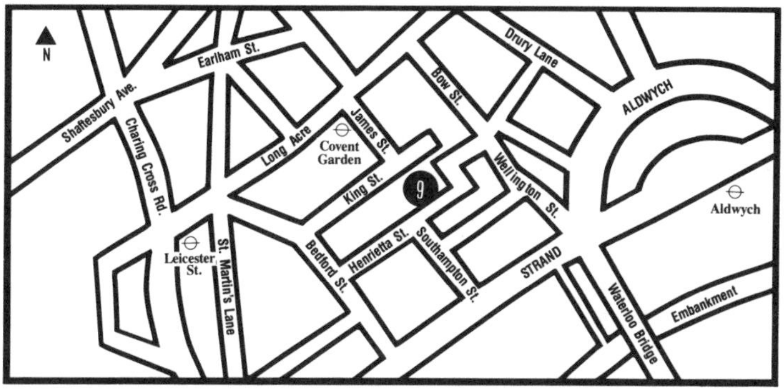

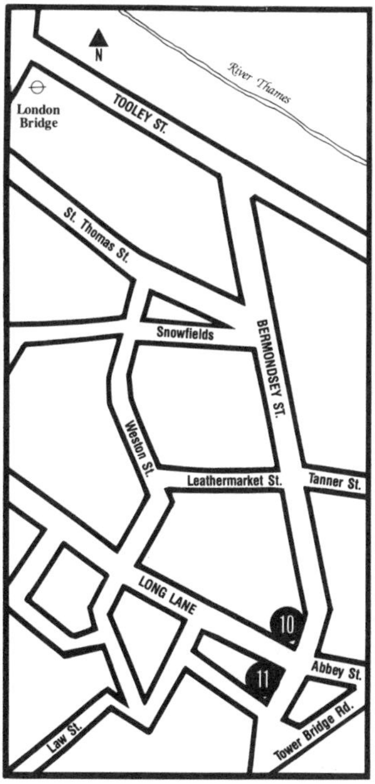

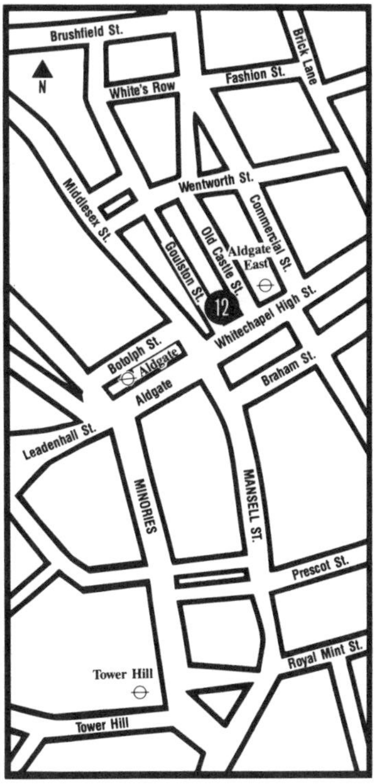

13 **Portobello Markets**

14 **The Mall**

⊖ **Underground Stations**

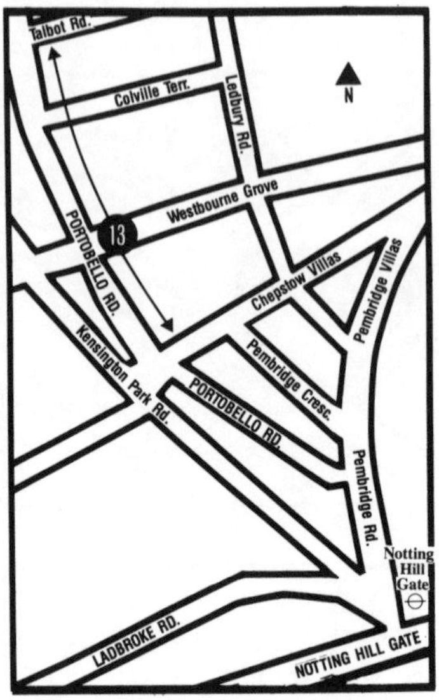

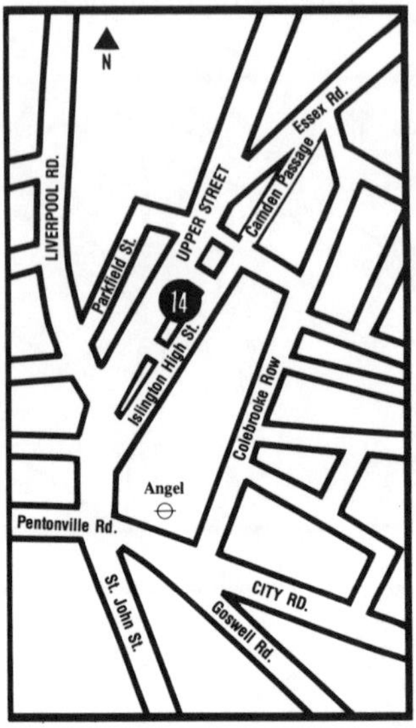

For advertising rates and free listing information please contact:

PAIGE PUBLICATIONS

P.O. Box 1384

Rancho Mirage, California 92270

Tel: 619 321 0174 or 619 328 7898

ANTIQUE MAPS

By Bruce Marsden

I would be amazed if you did not consult a map before you travelled to London — and you'll certainly need one once you are there. If maps had not been invented, just think what a huge complicated book would be required to describe in words what is plain to see on a map. What, then, is a map? Quite simply, a collection of symbols or graphic representations drawn on a flat surface to show part of the earth's surface. It is not surprising, therefore, that such a useful shorthand method of providing complex information should have a long history - certainly as far back as cave drawings, say forty thousand years ago. However, it is only since the introduction of paper and printing presses in the mid-1400's that maps started to become generally available, albeit to only a tiny minority of Europeans.

For the first century of printed maps, wood and copper were used to engrave the map upon, prior to inking and printing on a hand press. Hence the terms "woodblock" and "copperplate". Each has its characteristic appearance — best seen

ORIGINAL ANTIQUE MAPS

Something To Treasure For Always

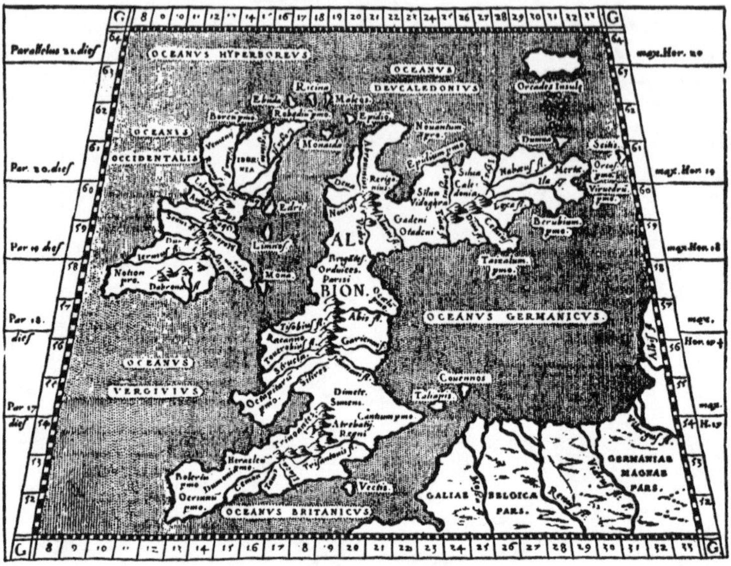

BRITISH ISLES - G. Porro, 1598

Perhaps the most appealing thing about an original antique map is the way in which it fires the imagination with images of centuries ago. Or perhaps it's the sheer beauty of the illustration which must have taken so many manhours. Wherever its appeal lies, an original antique map is something to be enjoyed, as well as being an investment.

Cartographia, formerly of Covent Garden, is one of the world's finest antique map galleries. Step inside to see maps from the 15th to the 19th centuries of all corners of the globe and all are guaranteed original. Alternatively send off for a descriptive list of maps of the areas of your interest. Catalogues issued from time to time.

Cartographia
limited

Pied Bull Yard
Bury Place
Bloomsbury, London W.C.1.
Telephone: 01 240 5687

in a museum or reputable map gallery, rather than reading about. Maps from this period of areas in demand are not commonly found.

In 1570 the first atlas (as we use the term today) was produced by Abraham Ortelius in Antwerp. Running to an incredible 4 separate issues in the first year, this book of maps was an immediate bestseller and continued so for about 50 years. The first maps in ths atlas were the world and four continents — Africa, the Americas, Asia and Europe: Australia was thought to exist but had not yet been discovered by Europeans. Many of these early maps were coloured by hand at the time of publication, though most were not. Provided examples exist of maps with 'original colour', an uncoloured map recently coloured in the appropriate manner is usually acceptable except to the most fastidious of collectors.

Continuing the tradition of mapmaking in the Low Countries in addition to Ortelius there was Mercator, the families Hondius, Jansson and Blaeu, taking us to about 1670. The period 1620-1670 is usually regarded as the great age of mapmaking as the maps were nearly always decorative as well as functional. Decoration include coats of arms, ships, monsters, animals, trees, ornate title pieces, lettering and many other features.

With Dutch connections, the great English mapmaker John Speed also published during this period. His famous map of the Americas, 1627, was the first atlas map to portray California as an island and thereby popularised this geographical curiosity. For more than a century this notion held sway.

The early exploration of California is particularly interesting with the Spanish pushing north from the south, the Russians reaching as far south as Los Angeles, and the Americans coming overland from the east. When Captain Cook was sent to explore the Pacific basin in the 1760's and 70's, a new westward prospect was gained for California which contributes greatly to the richness of the cultural heritage of the State.

The 1700's were dominated first by the French (Jaillot, de l'Isle, Vaugondy, Bellin) and the English (Seller, Moll, Popple, Mitchell, Jefferys). The latter particularly with their sailing charts reflecting the growing world-wide empire dependent on secure sea routes.

Whilst the eastern seaboard of north America had been charted since the early 1500's (with varying degrees of accuracy), penetration of the interior took place in earnest during the 1700's, stemming mainly from the great waterways. And by the 1700's German mapmakers were providing maps for the growing German market (Homann, Seutter, Lotter).

With the independence of the U.S., 1783, reliance on English printing began to be supplanted by indigenous craftsmen, and very soon atlases of states and maps of towns were being produced, as well as world atlases. Some of these examples of early American printing are now highly prized, such as atlases by Carey, Reid, Tanner, Finley. Because of the improved technology of printing, developed as part of the Industrial Revolution, most early American atlases are not rare because many were printed at the time.

The main generators for pricing are desirability and availability. A desirable item such as a city plan may be comparatively inexpensive as probably many were printed. Whereas a plan of a town at a very early stage of its development may be highly priced as only a very few prints would have been made because the market would have been restricted at that early time.

A word about condition. Unless a map is rare, try to buy maps only in good condition - no tears or creases, no splodged paint, no wormholes, full margins and cleanly printed. Do not be put off by maps with a central fold — these were usually folded by the printers to be bound into an atlas. Also many maps were folded (and sometimes mounted onto linen) to fit the pocket.

Finally, as with all genuine antiques, fine maps are getting harder to find. The supply is reducing and the desire to own genuine originals is increasing; expecially so with maps of the Americas as awareness of 'roots' and personal travel increases.

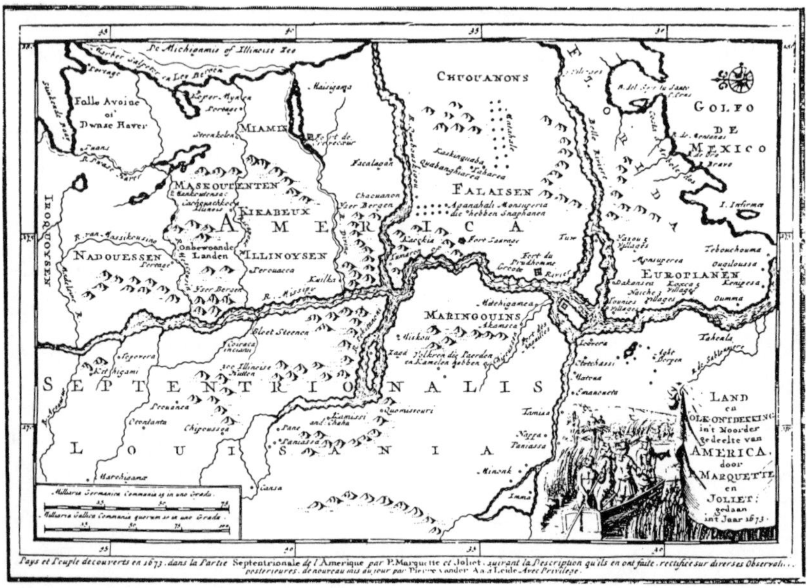

Bruce Marsden is an English architect, a Fellow of the Royal Geographical Society, and founder of Cartographia Ltd. — a premier source for the world's finest antique maps.

LONDON POSTAL DISTRICTS

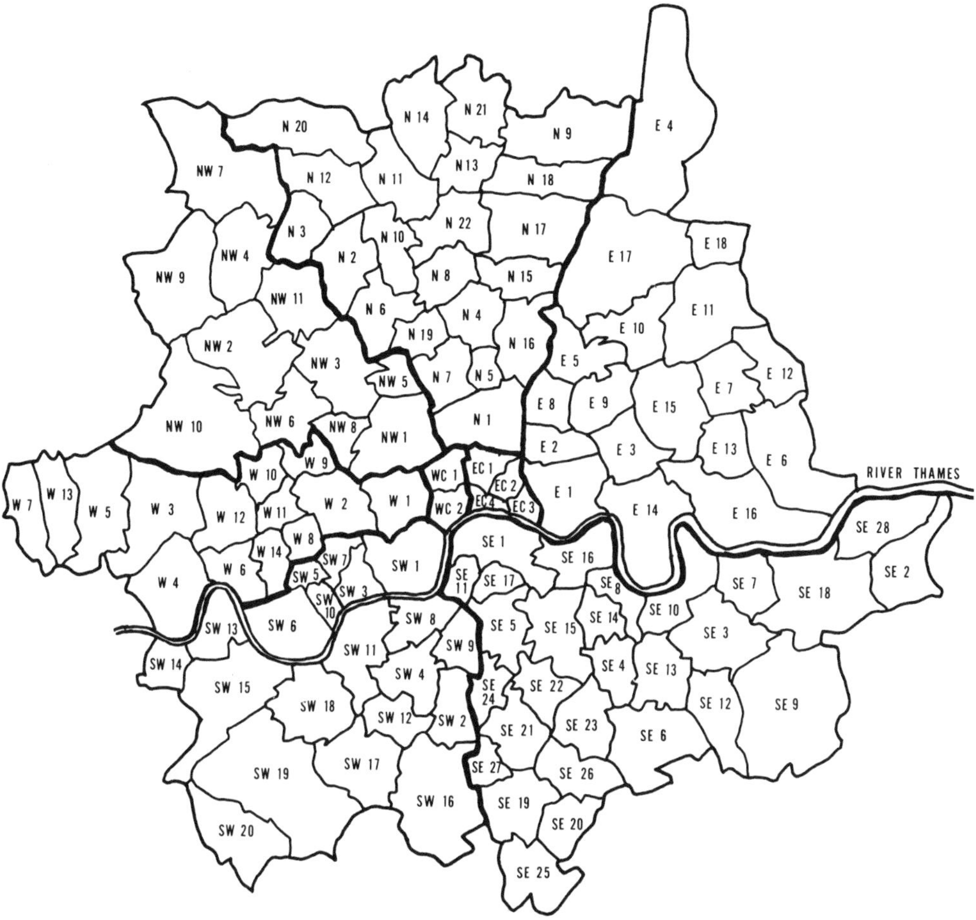

W.1. Mayfair, St. James's
W.2. Bayswater
W.3. Acton
W.4. Chiswick
W.5. Ealing
W.6. Hammersmith
W.8. Kensington
W.9. Maida Vale
W.11. Notting Hill
W.13. Ealing
W.14. West Kensington
S.W.1. Belgravia, Victoria
S.W.3. Chelsea, Knightsbridge
S.W.5. Earl's Court
S.W.6. Fulham
S.W.7. Knightsbridge, Sth. Kensington
S.W.8. Battersea
S.W.10. West Brompton
S.W.11. Battersea, Clapham
S.W.13. Barnes
S.W.14. East Sheen, Mortlake
S.W.15. Putney
S.W.16. Streatham
S.W.19. Wimbledon
S.W.20. Raynes Park
S.E.1. Southwark
S.E.5. Camberwell
S.E.6. Catford
S.E.10. Greenwich
S.E.13. Lewisham
S.E.15. Peckham
S.E.18. Plumstead
S.E.21. West Dulwich
S.E.26. Sydenham
E.1. Whitechapel
E.17. Walthamstow
E.C.1. Holborn
E.C.3. City of London
W.C.1. Bloomsbury
W.C.2. Holborn, Strand
N.1. Islington
N.2. East Finchley
N.3. Finchley
N.4. Crouch Hill, Finsbury Park
N.5. Highbury
N.6. Highgate
N.7. Holloway
N.11. New Southgate
N.12. North Finchley
N.16. Highbury
N.19. Upper Holloway
N.20. Whetstone
N.21. Southgate, Winchmore Hill
N.W.1. Camden Town, Regent's Park
N.W.2. Cricklewood
N.W.3. Hampstead
N.W.4. Hendon
N.W.5. Kentish Town
N.W.6. West Hampstead, Kilburn
N.W.7. Edgware, Mill Hill
N.W.8. Marylebone, St. John's Wood
N.W.10. Kensal Rise, Willesden

W.1. Mayfair, St. James's

A.D.C. HERITAGE LTD.
2 Old Bond Street Tel.493 5088
Silver, Sheffield plate.

AARON GALLERY
34 Bruton Street Tel.499 9434
Carpets, ancient art.

ARTHUR ACKERMANN & SON LTD.
3 Old Bond Street Tel.493 3288
Sporting pictures, prints.

ADAMS
2 Royal Arcade, 28 Old Bond Street Tel.629 0717
Porcelain.

THOMAS AGNEW & SONS LTD.
43 Old Bond Street Tel.629 6176
Paintings, watercolors.

ALEXANDER AND BERENDT LTD.
1a Davies Street Tel.499 4775
French furniture.

ANTIQUE PORCELAIN CO. LTD.
149 New Bond Street Tel.629 1254
Porcelain, French furniture.

PHILIP ANTROBUS
11 New Bond Street Tel.493 4557
Jewelry.

ARENSKI
29-31 George Street Tel.486 0678
Furniture, bronzes, clocks, glass.

ARMITAGE
4 Davies Street Tel.408 0675
Silver.

ARMOUR-WINSTON LTD.
43 Burlington Arcade Tel.493 8937
Jewelry, clocks.

ASPREY & CO.
165-169 New Bond Street Tel.493 6767
Furniture, silver, clocks.

AVAKIAN ORIENTAL CARPETS LTD.
20 Davies Street Tel.493 5758
Carpets.

BARLING OF MOUNT STREET LTD.
112 Mount Street Tel.499 2858
Furniture, Oriental works of art.

J. & A. BEARE LTD.
7 Broadwick Street Tel.437 1449
Musical instruments.

PAUL BENNETT
75 George Street Tel.935 1555
Silver, Sheffield plate.

BENTLEY AND CO. LTD.
65 New Bond Street Tel.629 0651
Jewelry.

BERNHEIMER FINE ARTS LTD.
32 St. George Street, Mayfair Tel.499 0293
European furniture & works of art, 17-19 C. Oriental porcelain.

H. BLAIRMAN AND SONS LTD.
119 Mount Street Tel.493 0444
18th C furniture.

ANNE BLOOM
10a New Bond Street Tel.493 0526
Jewelry, silver.

N. BLOOM & SONS (ANTIQUES) LTD.
40/41 Conduit Street Tel.629 5060
Silver, clocks, bronzes, jewelry.

BLUETT & SONS LTD.
48 Davies Street Tel.629 3397
Oriental works of art.

BLUNDERBUSS ANTIQUES
29 Thayer Street Tel.486 2444
Arms and armour.

BOBINET LTD.
102 Mount Street Tel.408 0333
Clocks, watches, furniture.

BOND STREET ANTIQUE CENTRE
124 New Bond Street . . . . see page 26

BOND STREET SILVER GALLERIES
111-112 New Bond Street . . . . see page 26

BRUFORD & HEMING LTD.
28 Conduit Street Tel.499 7644
Jewelry, silver-especially flatware.

BURLINGTON GALLERY LTD.
10 Burlington Gardens Tel.734 9228
Prints, maps.

BURLINGTON PAINTINGS LTD.
12 Burlington Gardens Tel.734 9984
Watercolors, paintings.

PETER CAMERON
4 Grosvenor Street Tel.491 8949
Silver, Sheffield plate.

CARRINGTON & CO. LTD
170 Regent Street Tel.734 3727
Silver, jewelry, clocks, watches.

LUMLEY CAZALET LTD.
24 Davies Street Tel.499 5058
Late 19th and 20th C original prints-Matisse, Picasso, Chagall, etc.

J. CHRISTIE
26 Burlington Arcade Tel.629 3070
Silver, bronzes, jewelry.

CLARENDON GALLERY
8 Vigo Street..Tel.439 4557
Watercolors, paintings.

COLEFAX & FOWLER
39 Brook Street..Tel.493 2231
18th-19th C furniture, carpets.

COLLINGWOOD OF CONDUIT STREET
46 Conduit Street..Tel.734 2656
Silver, jewelry.

COLNAGHI
14 Old Bond Street...Tel.491 7408
Watercolors, paintings, sculpture.

CROWTHER OF SYON LODGE
6 Old Bond Street..Tel.493 8688
Bronze & marble statues, panelled rooms.

THE CURIO SHOP
21 Shepherd Market...Tel.493 5616
Metalware, prints, glass, china.

A.B. DAVIS LTD.
18 Brook Street..Tel.629 1053
Jewelry, silver.

DEMAS
31 Burlington Arcade...Tel.493 9496
Jewelry.

DENISA THE LADY NEWBOROUGH
1-2 Whitehorse Street, Shepherd Market...............................Tel.493 3954
Jewelry, silver.

CHARLES EDE LTD.
37 Brook Street..Tel.493 4944
Antiquities.

EMANOUEL ANTIQUES LTD.
64 South Audley Street...Tel.493 4350
Furniture, carpets, Islamic art.

ESKENAZI LTD.
Foxglove House, 166 Piccadilly.......................................Tel.493 5464
Oriental works of art.

BRIAN FIELDEN
3 New Cavendish Street...Tel.935 6912
Furniture, barometers, mirrors.

THE FINE ART SOCIETY
148 New Bond Street..Tel.629 5116
Watercolors, paintings, sculpture.

I. FREEMAN & SON, SIMON KAYE LTD.
18 Dover Street..Tel.493 7658
Medical instruments, silver, Sheffield plate.

FROST & REED LTD.
41 New Bond Street...Tel.629 2457
Watercolors, paintings.

GARRARD & CO. LTD.
112 Regent Street........Tel.734 7020
Silver, Sheffield plate, jewelry, clocks.

CHRISTOPHER GIBBS LTD.
118 New Bond Street........Tel.629 2008
Furniture, paintings.

THOMAS GIBSON FINE ART LTD.
9a New Bond Street........Tel.499 8572
Paintings, sculpture.

THE GOLDEN PAST
6 Brook Street........Tel.493 6422
Jewelry, silver.

THOMAS GOODE & CO.
19 South Audley Street........Tel.499 2823
Porcelain, pottery, Oriental works of art.

A. & F. GORDON
120a Mount Street........Tel.499 5596
Furniture, bronzes, paintings.

GRAUS ANTIQUES
125 New Bond Street........Tel.629 6680
Jewelry, watches, enamels.

GRAYS ANTIQUE MARKET
58 Davies Street........see page 28

GRAYS MEWS
1-7 Davies Mews........see page 28

RICHARD GREEN (FINE PAINTINGS)
36 and 44 Dover Street........Tel.493 3939
4 New Bond Street........Tel.491 3277
Paintings.

SIMON GRIFFIN ANTIQUES
3 Royal Arcade, Old Bond Street........Tel.491 7367
Silver, Sheffield plate.

GRIMALDI
12 Royal Arcade, Old Bond Street........Tel.493 3953
Barometers, clocks, watches.

HAHN & SON FINE ART DEALERS
47 Albemarle Street........Tel.493 9196
Paintings.

M. HAKIM
4 Royal Arcade, Old Bond Street........Tel.629 2643
Jewelry, enamels, snuff boxes.

HALCYON DAYS
14 Brook Street........Tel.629 8811
Georgian antique enamels, prints, papier mâché.

HANCOCKS & CO. (JEWELLERS) LTD.
1 Burlington Gardens........Tel.493 8904
Jewelry, silver, Sheffield plate.

HARRIS (ANTIQUES) LTD.
17-18 Old Bond Street....Tel.499 0352
Silver, Sheffield plate, jewelry.

NICHOLAS HARRIS
26 Conduit Street....Tel.499 5991
Jewelry, silver.

HARVEY & GORE (ANTIQUES) LTD.
4 Burlington Gardens....Tel.493 2714
Jewelry, silver, Sheffield plate.

W.R. HARVEY & CO. (ANTIQUES) LTD.
5 Old Bond Street....Tel.499 8385
Furniture, clocks.

BRIAN HAUGHTON ANTIQUES
3b Burlington Gardens....Tel.734 5491
Porcelain, pottery.

JEANETTE HAYHURST FINE GLASS
3b Burlington Gardens....Tel.437 4975
Decanters, perfume bottles, table glass.

HEIRLOOM & HOWARD LTD.
1 Hay Hill....Tel.493 5868
Porcelain, paintings.

HENNELL LTD.
12 New Bond Street....Tel.629 6888
Jewelry, silver, Sheffield plate.

M. HESKIA
19 Mount Street....Tel.629 1483
Oriental carpets & rugs.

HOLMES LTD.
29 Old Bond Street....Tel.493 1396
Jewelry, silver, Sheffield plate.

HOWARD ANTIQUES
8 Davies Street....Tel.629 2628
Furniture.

HUDSON & WILLIAMS
14 Crawford Street....Tel.935 7627
Furniture.

JADIS
43 Davies Street....Tel.629 2141
Carpets, bronzes, jewelry, paintings.

THE JEWEL HOUSE (MAYFAIR)
23 Lansdowne Row....Tel.499 7936
Jewelry

C. JOHN (RARE RUGS) LTD.
70 South Audley Street....Tel.493 5288
Carpets, tapestries.

JOHNSON, WALKER & TOLHURST LTD.
64 Burlington Arcade....Tel.629 2615
Jewelry, silver.

ALEXANDER JURAN & CO.
74 New Bond Street....Tel.629 2550
Carpets, tapestries.

KENNEDY CARPETS
9a Vigo Street....Tel.439 8873
Oriental carpets and kelims.

KHALILI GALLERY
15c Clifford Street....Tel.734 4202
Islamic works of art.

D.S. LAVENDER ANTIQUES LTD.
16b Grafton Street....Tel.629 1782
Silver, jewelry, snuff boxes.

RONALD A. LEE (FINE ARTS) LTD.
1-9 Bruton Place....Tel.629 5600
Furniture, clocks, barometers, armour.

THE LEGER GALLERIES LTD.
13 Old Bond Street....Tel.629 3538
Paintings, watercolors.

M. & L. SILVER CO. LTD.
2 Woodstock Street....Tel.499 5392
Silver.

MAAS GALLERY
15a Clifford Street....Tel.734 2302
Paintings, watercolors.

McALPINE ANCIENT ART
60 Brook Street....Tel.629 2247
Antiquities.

MacCONNAL MASON GALLERY
15 Burlington Arcade....Tel.499 6991
Paintings, prints.

MAGGS BROS. LTD.
50 Berkeley Square....Tel.493 7160
Books, manuscripts, autograph letters.

MALLETT AT BOURDON HOUSE LTD.
2 Davies Street....Tel.629 2444
Furniture, clocks, garden statuary, objets d'art.

MALLETT & SON (ANTIQUES) LTD.
40 New Bond Street....Tel.499 7411
17th-19th C furniture, clocks, china, decorative pictures.

D.M. & P. MANHEIM LTD.
69 Upper Berkeley Street....Tel.723 6595
Porcelain, pottery, enamels.

MANSOUR GALLERY
46 Davies Street....Tel.491 7444
Antiquities.

MARKS ANTIQUES LTD.
49 Curzon Street....Tel.499 1788
Silver, Sheffield plate.

MASSADA ANTIQUES
45 New Bond Street....Tel.493 4792
Jewelry, silver.

MAYFAIR CARPET GALLERY LTD.
8 Old Bond Street....Tel.493 0126
Carpets & rugs.

MAYFAIR MICROSCOPES LTD.
64 Burlington Arcade....Tel.629 2616
Microscopes, telescopes.

MAYFAIR VILLAGE ANTIQUES
19 Shepherd Market, Mayfair....Tel.493 4796
Silver, glass, jewelry, brass.

NIGEL MILNE LTD.
16c Grafton Street....Tel.493 9646
Jewelry, silver frames.

JOHN MITCHELL & SONS
8 New Bond Street....Tel.493 7567
Paintings, watercolors, prints.

PAUL MITCHELL LTD.
99 New Bond Street....Tel.493 8732
Picture frames.

SYDNEY L. MOSS LTD.
51 Brook Street....Tel.629 4670
Oriental works of art.

MOUNT ST. GALLERIES
125 Mount Street....Tel.493 5211
Furniture, paintings.

RICHARD MUNDEY
19 Chiltern Street....Tel.935 5613
Pewter.

KENNETH NEAME LTD.
25 Brook Street....Tel.629 0445
18th-19th C furniture.

Marks Antiques Ltd.

We specialize in antique
and reproduction silver
and silver plate.

49 Curzon Street. London W.1
Telephone: 01-499 1788

NEPTUNE ANTIQUES
99 Mount Street Tel.499 2002
Furniture.

L. NEWLAND & SON
17 Picton Place Tel.935 2864
Jewelry, objets d'art. Repairs & restoration.

RICHARD OGDEN LTD.
28-29 Burlington Arcade Tel.493 9136
Jewelry, silver, Sheffield plate.

THE PARKER GALLERY
12a-12b Berkeley Street Tel.499 5906
Paintings, prints, model ships, drawings.

PARTRIDGE (FINE ARTS) LTD.
144-146 New Bond Street Tel.629 0834
Furniture, silver, paintings.

W.H. PATTERSON FINE ARTS LTD.
19 Albemarle Street Tel.629 4119
Paintings.

HOWARD PHILLIPS
11a Henrietta Place Tel.580 9844
Glass.

RONALD PHILLIPS LTD.
26 Bruton Street Tel.493 2341
Furniture.

S.J. PHILLIPS LTD.
139 New Bond Street Tel.629 6261
Jewelry, silver.

PORTMAN CARPETS
7 Portman Square Tel.486 3770
Carpets, rugs, kelims.

JONATHAN POTTER LTD.
1 Grafton Street Tel.491 3520
Maps, prints, atlases.

BERNARD QUARITCH LTD.
5-8 Lower John Street Tel.734 2983
Antiquarian books.

RABI GALLERY
94 Mount Street Tel.499 8886
Islamic works of art.

WILLIAM REDFORD
9 Mount Street Tel.629 1165
French furniture, bronzes, procelain.

ANTHONY REED
3 Cork Street Tel.437 0157
Paintings, watercolors.

DAVID RICHARDS & SONS
12 New Cavendish Street Tel.935 3206
Silver, Sheffield plate.

GERALD SATTIN LTD.
25 Burlington Arcade.......Tel.493 6557
Porcelain, glass, silver.

CHAS J. SAWYER
1 Grafton Street.......Tel.493 3810
Books, manuscripts.

SCHWARTZ SACKIN & CO. LTD.
57-60 Piccadilly.......Tel.409 1359
Fine art and eccentricities.

B.A. SEABY LTD.
8 Cavendish Square.......Tel.631 3707
Coins, medals.

SIMEON
19 Burlington Arcade.......Tel.493 3353
Jewelry, snuff bottles, netsuke.

THE SLADMORE GALLERY
32 Bruton Place.......Tel.499 0365
Bronzes.

SOMERVILLE & SIMPSON
11 Savile Row.......Tel.437 5414
Paintings, watercolors, prints.

HENRY SOTHERAN LTD.
2-5 Sackville Street.......Tel.734 1150
Antiquarian books, prints.

SOUTH AUDLEY ART GALLERIES LTD.
36 South Audley Street.......Tel.499 3178
Furniture, clocks, bronzes, paintings.

JOHN SPARKS LTD.
128 Mount Street.......Tel.499 2265
Oriental works of art.

A. & J. SPEELMAN
129 Mount Street.......Tel.499 5126
Oriental works of art.

EDWARD SPEELMAN LTD.
175 Piccadilly.......Tel.493 0657
Paintings.

H.J. SPILLER LTD.
37 Beak Street.......Tel.437 4661
Paintings, picture frames.

STAIR & CO. LTD.
120 Mount Street.......Tel.499 1784
18th C Eng. furniture.

TESSIERS LTD.
26 New Bond Street.......Tel.629 0458
Jewelry, silver, Sheffield plate.

TOOLEY ADAMS & CO. LTD.
83 Marylebone High Street.......Tel.486 9052 / 935 5855
Antiquarian maps, atlases, prints, reference books.

VENNERS ANTIQUES
7 New Cavendish Street Tel.935 0184
Porcelain, pottery.

VIGO CARPET GALLERY
6a Vigo Street Tel.439 6971
Oriental carpets & rugs.

VIGO-STERNBERG GALLERIES
37 South Audley Street Tel.629 8307
Oriental carpets & rugs, tapestries.

WARTSKI LTD.
14 Grafton Street Tel.493 1141
Jewelry, silver, Russian works of art.

WILLIAMS & SON
2 Grafton Street Tel.493 4985
Paintings.

HENRY WILLIS (ANTIQUE SILVER)
4 Grosvenor Street Tel.491 8949
Silver.

"YOUNG STEPHEN" LTD.
1 Burlington Gardens, New Bond Street Tel.499 7927
Jewelry, silver.

W.2. Bayswater

ANTIQUUS A.G.
17 Pembridge, Square . . . . by appointment Tel.229 0224
Country furniture, tapestries.

PETER BENTLEY
22 Connaught Street Tel.723 9394
Furniture.

CLAUDE BORNOFF
20 Chepstow Corner, Pembridge Villas Tel.229 8947
Furniture, porcelain, metalware, bronzes.

CONNAUGHT GALLERIES
44 Connaught Street Tel.723 1660
Furniture, porcelain.

A.B. DAVIS LTD.
89-91 Queensway Tel.229 2777
Jewelry, silver.

M. McALEER
32a Sussex Place Tel.723 5794
Silver, jewelry.

MARK GALLERY
9 Porchester Place Tel.262 4906
Icons.

THE PINE HOUSE
1 Pembridge Villas Tel.221 7044
Furniture.

W.3. Acton

WOODS WAREHOUSE
371 Horn Lane....................Tel.992 2234
General antiques.

W.4. Chiswick

CHISWICK ANTIQUES
Fisher's Lane....................Tel.995 2967
Furniture, silver, china, glass.

CHISWICK FIREPLACES
62 South Parade....................Tel.994 2981
Victorian fireplaces.

GOODALL & CO. LTD.
24-26 Chiswick High Road....................Tel.994 1729
Furniture, maps, prints.

STRAND ANTIQUES
166 Thames Road, Strand-on-the-Green....................Tel.994 1912
General antiques.

STRATTON-QUINN ANTIQUES ETC.
164 Thames Road, Strand-on-the-Green....................Tel.994 3140
Furniture.

WEST LONDON ANTIQUES
160 Chiswick High Road....................Tel.995 4166
Furniture.

W.5. Ealing

THE BADGER
12 St. Mary's Road....................Tel.567 5601
Furniture, clocks.

EALING GALLERY
112 Pitshanger Lane....................Tel.997 3108
Paintings, watercolors.

W.6. Hammersmith

N. DAVIGHI
117 Shepherd's Bush Road....................Tel.603 5357
General antiques, chandeliers.

QUESTOR ANTIQUES
295 King Street....................Tel.741 3822
General antiques.

M.L. WAROUJIAN
110-112 Hammersmith Road....................Tel.748 7509
Oriental carpets & rugs.

AL MASHREQ GALLERIES
110 Kensington Church Street. Tel.229 5453
Islamic antiques.

THE ANTIQUE HOME
104a Kensington Church Street. Tel.229 5892
Furniture.

EDDY BARDAWIL
106 Kensington Church Street. Tel.221 3967
Furniture, brass, prints.

BAUMKOTTER GALLERY
63a Kensington Church Street. Tel.937 5171
17th-19th C oil paintings.

ANTHONY BELTON
14 Holland Street. Tel.937 1012
Pottery, marine items.

BONROSE ANTIQUES
172 Kensington Church Street. Tel.229 5468
Furniture, clocks, bronzes.

MAURICE BRAHAM LTD.
131 Kensington Church Street. Tel.727 6878
Antiquities

DAVID BROWER ANTIQUES
113 Kensington Church Street. Tel.221 4155
Porcelain, furniture, bronzes, clocks.

SIMON CASTLE
38b Kensington Church Street. Tel.937 2268
Decorative carvings, treen.

CATHAY ANTIQUES
12 Thackeray Street. Tel.937 6066
Oriental antiques.

CHURCH STREET GALLERIES LTD.
77 Kensington Church Street. Tel.937 2461
17th-19th C furniture.

AUBREY J. COLEMAN ANTIQUES
121 Kensington Church Street. Tel.221 6228
Furniture, pictures, chess sets.

BELINDA COOTE ANTIQUES
29 Holland Street. Tel.937 3924
Tapestries, porcelain, pottery.

R.O. & F. COYLE
10 Holland Street. Tel.937 3723
American & European folk art.

MRS. M.E. CRICK LTD.
166 Kensington Church Street. Tel.229 1338
Chandeliers.

DAVIES ANTIQUES
44a Kensington Church Street. Tel.937 9216
Porcelain, maps, prints.

DELOMOSNE & SON LTD.
4 Campden Hill Road....Tel.937 1804
Glass, porcelain, pottery.

RICHARD DENNIS
144 Kensington Church Street....Tel.727 2061
Pottery.

H. & W. DEUTSCH ANTIQUES
111 Kensington Church Street....Tel.727 5984
Porcelain, silver, bronzes.

PHILIP & BERNARD DOMBEY
174 Kensington Church Street....Tel.229 7100
French clocks.

ETNA ANTIQUES
81 Kensington Church Street....Tel.937 3754
18th-19th C furniture.

MICHAEL C. GERMAN
38b Kensington Church Street....Tel.937 2771
Arms, armour, walking sticks.

GRAHAM & OXLEY (ANTIQUES) LTD.
101 Kensington Church Street....Tel.229 1850
Porcelain, pottery.

EILA GRAHAME
97c Kensington Church Street....Tel.727 4132
Glass, needlework, porcelain, prints.

GREEN'S ANTIQUE GALLERIES
117 Kensington Church Street....Tel.229 9618
Jewelry, dolls, china, furniture.

GROSVENOR ANTIQUES LTD.
27 Holland Street....Tel.937 8649
Porcelain, pottery.

ROBERT HALES ANTIQUES
133 Kensington Church Street....Tel.229 3887
Arms, armour.

JONATHAN HARRIS
54 Kensington Church Street....Tel.937 3133
Furniture, works of art.

HASLAM & WHITEWAY
105 Kensington Church Street....Tel.229 1145
Furniture.

HOFF ANTIQUES LTD.
66a Kensington Church Street....Tel.229 5516
Porcelain.

HOPE & GLORY
131a Kensington Church Street....Tel.727 8424
Royal commemorative china, glass.

JONATHAN HORNE
66b & 66c Kensington Church Street....Tel.221 5658
Pottery, metalware.

MELVYN JAY ANTIQUES
64a Kensington Church Street Tel.937 6832
Furniture, silver, clocks, bronzes.

HOWARD JONES
43 Kensington Church Street Tel.937 4359
Silver, procelain, jewelry.

R. & J. JONES
137 Kensington Church Street Tel.221 4026
Paintings, porcelain.

PETER KEMP
174a Kensington Church Street Tel.229 2988
Porcelain.

KENSINGTON FURNITURE BAZAAR
214/216 Kensington High Street Tel.937 4973
Furniture.

KLABER & KLABER
2a Bedford Gardens, Kensington Church Street Tel.727 4573
Porcelain, enamels.

THE LACQUER CHEST
75 Kensington Church Street Tel.937 1306
Furniture.

Visit

HOPE & GLORY

Royal commemorative china, glass and Royalty picture specialists

Open
Tuesday – Friday
10am-5pm
Saturday 10am-2.30pm

Closed Sunday and Monday

131a Kensington
Church Street,
London W8 7LP

Proprietor:
Ernest L. Titmuss

Tel: 01-727 8424

W.8.

FIONA & BILL LAIDLAW ANTIQUES
40 Gordon Place, Holland St. Tel.937 8493
Biedermeier furniture, majolica.

LEV (ANTIQUES) LTD.
97 Kensington Church Street Tel.727 9248
Jewelry, silver.

LIBRA ANTIQUES
131e Kensington Church Street Tel.727 2990
Pottery, lustre ware.

LINDSAY ANTIQUES
99 Kensington Church Street Tel.727 2333
Furniture, paintings, pottery.

ERIC LINEHAM & SONS
62 Kensington Church Street Tel.937 9650
Porcelain, clocks.

LITTLE WINCHESTER GALLERY
36a Kensington Church Street Tel.937 8444
Paintings.

C.H. MAJOR (ANTIQUES) LTD.
154 Kensington Church Street Tel.229 1162
Furniture.

Fine antiquarian books

15-20th Century

Large stock of all subjects

Restoration - Binding - Free Search Service

121a Kensington Church Street - London W8 7LP

Tel: 01 229 2033 or 01 221 8822

DAVID MALIK & SON LTD.
112 Kensington Church Street Tel.229 2987
Crystal chandeliers, wall brackets.

S. MARCHANT & SON
120 Kensington Church Street Tel.229 5319
Chinese porcelain, furniture.

J. & J. MAY
40 Kensington Church Street Tel.937 3575
Commemorative glass, porcelain, pottery.

D. MELLOR & A.L. BAXTER
121a Kensington Church Street Tel.229 2033
Antiquarian books - Science, medicine, travel, history.

D.C. MONK & SON
132-134 Kensington Church Street Tel.229 3727
Oriental porcelain.

OLIVER - SUTTON ANTIQUES
34c Kensington Church Street Tel.937 0633
Staffordshire pottery.

PEEL ANTIQUES
131d Kensington Church Street Tel.727 8298
Furniture, porcelain, pottery.

HENRY PHILLIPS
2 Campden Street Tel.727 4079
Furniture.

RAFFETY
34 Kensington Church Street Tel.938 1100
Clocks, watches, furniture.

JOHN REID
40a Kensington Church Street Tel.937 3379
Prints.

JOAN ROGER (ANTIQUES) LTD.
17 Uxbridge Street Tel.727 2227
Furniture, porcelain, pottery, prints.

WEST LONDON
Antiques Fair

1987 January 15-18
1987 August 13-16

Kensington Town Hall, Hornton St, W8

Adm. £2 incl. Catalogue

Enquiries:
PO Box 114
Haywards Heath, W. Sussex
Tel: 04447-2514

Penman Antiques Fairs

W.8.

ST. JUDE'S ANTIQUES
107 Kensington Church Street..Tel.727 8737
Porcelain, small furniture.

ARTHUR SEAGER ANTIQUES LTD.
25a Holland Street..Tel.937 3262
Furniture, pottery, pictures.

M. & D. SELIGMANN
37 Kensington Church Street..Tel.937 0400
Furniture, porcelain, pottery, enamels.

JEAN SEWELL (ANTIQUES) LTD.
3 Campden Street..Tel.727 3122
Porcelain, pottery, furniture.

SYLVIA SHEPPARD
71 Kensington Church Street..Tel.937 0965
Furniture.

SINAI ANTIQUES LTD.
221 Kensington Church Street..Tel.229 6190
Carpets, silver, paintings.

SIMON SPERO
109 Kensington Church Street..Tel.727 7413
Ceramics, watercolors.

CONSTANCE STOBO
31 Holland Street..Tel.937 6282
Pottery.

JACOB STODEL
116 Kensington Church Street..Tel.221 2652
Furniture, Oriental works of art.

PAMELA TEIGNMOUTH & SON
108 Kensington Church Street..Tel.229 1602
18th-19th C furniture, papier mâché, tôleware.

MURRAY THOMSON LTD.
141 Kensington Church Street..Tel.727 1727
Furniture.

THE WINTER PALACE
69 Kensington Church Street..Tel.937 2410
Russian works of art.

MARY WISE
27 Holland Street..Tel.937 8649
Porcelain, furniture, pictures.

W.9. Maida Vale

FLUSS & CHARLESWORTH LTD.
1 Lauderdale Road..Tel.286 8339
Furniture.

EDWARD SALTI
77 Wellesley Court..Tel.286 3106
18th C enamel boxes.

ALBION FINE ART
61 Ledbury Road..Tel.221 2977
17th-19th C paintings.

ALICE'S
86 Portobello Road...Tel.229 8187
General antiques.

THE ANTIQUE TEXTILE COMPANY
100 Portland Road..Tel.221 7730
Period costume, lace.

AXIA
43 Pembridge Villas......................by appointment......................Tel.727 9724
Islamic & Byzantine works of art.

SERGE BAILLACHE
189 Westbourne Grove...Tel.229 2270
Furniture.

BARHAM FINE ART
83 Portobello Road...Tel.727 3845
Furniture, porcelain, clocks, bronzes, paintings.

P.R. BARHAM
111 Portobello Road..Tel.727 3397
Furniture, porcelain, silver.

DAVID BLACK ORIENTAL CARPETS
96 Portland Road..Tel.727 2566
Carpets and rugs.

BLAKE ANTIQUES
216 Westbourne Grove..Tel.229 3232
Furniture, clocks.

F.E.A. BRIGGS, LTD.
73 & 77 Ledbury Road..Tel.727 0909
Furniture, clocks, scientific instruments.

HELEN BUXTON ANTIQUES
193 Westbourne Grove..Tel.229 9997
Oriental ceramics, furniture.

CAELT GALLERY
182 Westbourne Grove..Tel.229 9309
Paintings.

CANONBURY ANTIQUES LTD.
174 Westbourne Grove..Tel.229 2786
Furniture, clocks, porcelain, bronzes.

JACK CASIMIR LTD.
23 Pembridge Road...Tel.727 8643
Brass, copper, pewter.

CASSIO ANTIQUES
68 Ledbury Road..Tel.727 0678
Furniture.

COCOZZA ANTIQUES
208 Westbourne Grove..Tel.221 1535
Fine furniture, works of art.

COHEN & PEARCE
84 Portobello Road..Tel.229 9458
Oriental works of art.

FRANK COLLINS ANTIQUES
60 Ledbury Road..Tel.221 7108
General antiques.

THE CORNER PORTOBELLO ANTIQUES SUPERMARKET
282-290 Westbourne Grove..see page 26

JOHN DALE
87 Portobello Road..Tel.727 1304
General antiques.

MICHAEL DAVIDSON
52 & 54 Ledbury Road..Tel.229 6088
Furniture, objets d'art.

PETER & DANIELE DODD
66 Ledbury Road..Tel.221 4727
Furniture, paintings.

DODO OLD ADVERTISING
3 Denbigh Road..Tel.229 3132
Posters, signs, pub mirrors.

E. & A. ANTIQUES
36 Ledbury Road..Tel.229 1823
Silver, plate, furniture.

MARTIN EDWARDS
14 Needham Road..Tel.221 0417
Georgian silver, furniture.

ELGIN ANTIQUES
123 Portobello Road..Tel.727 9852
General antiques.

THE FACADE
196 Westbourne Grove..Tel.727 2159
Furniture, lighting.

JACK FAIRMAN (CARPETS) LTD.
218 Westbourne Grove..Tel.229 2262
Carpets and rugs.

KEITH FINCH
187 Westbourne Grove..Tel.229 0267
Furniture.

JUDY FOX ANTIQUES
81 Portobello Road..Tel.229 8130
Furniture, porcelain.

J. FREEMAN
85a Portobello Road..Tel.221 5076
Silver, Sheffield plate.

GAVIN GRAHAM GALLERY
47 Ledbury Road..Tel.229 4848
Paintings, watercolors.

L. GUERRA ANTIQUES
82 Portobello Road....................Tel.727 0374
General antiques. Trade only.

HIRST ANTIQUES
59 Pembridge Road....................Tel.727 9364
Oak furniture.

JOHN HOOKE & SON
214 Westbourne Grove....................Tel.229 1050
General antiques.

HYDE PARK ANTIQUES
191 Westbourne Grove....................Tel.727 1585
Silver.

A. IBBA
64 Ledbury Road....................Tel.243 0787
General antiques.

OLIVIA JACKSON
287 Westbourne Grove....................Tel.727 2817
Furniture, porcelain, silver.

GEORGE JOHNSON ANTIQUES
120 Kensington Park Road....................Tel.229 3119
Furniture, barometers, clocks, bronzes.

KRYSTYNA ANTIQUES
190 Westbourne Grove....................Tel.727 2699
Furniture.

LACY GALLERY
38-40 Ledbury Road....................Tel.229 9105
Paintings, watercolors, prints.

S. LAMPARD & SON LTD.
32 Notting Hill Gate....................Tel.229 5457
Jewelry, silver, clocks.

J. LIPITCH LTD.
177 Westbourne Grove....................Tel.229 0783
Furniture, clocks, porcelain, bronzes.

LONDON INTERNATIONAL SILVER CO. LTD.
82 Portobello Road....................Tel.221 1071
Silver, plate, flatware.

LONDON POSTCARD CENTRE
21 Kensington Park Road....................Tel.229 1888
Postcards, paintings, watercolors.

ROBIN MARTIN
44 Ledbury Road....................Tel.727 1301
General antiques.

MERCURY ANTIQUES
1 Ladbroke Road....................Tel.727 5106
Porcelain, pottery, glass.

S. MESSIM
63a Ledbury Road....................Tel.727 1706
Furniture.

SYLVIA NAPIER LTD.
32 Ledbury Road Tel.229 9986
Furniture.

ORMONDE GALLERY
156 Portobello Road Tel.229 9800
Oriental items.

E.S. PHILLIPS & SON
99 Portobello Road Tel.229 2113
General antiques.

RICHARD PHILP
59 Ledbury Road Tel.727 7915
Furniture, works of art.

PORTOBELLO SILVER COMPANY
82 Portobello Road Tel.221 1071
Pine furniture.

PRINCEDALE ANTIQUES
70 Princedale Road Tel.727 0868
Country furniture.

A. RAPHAEL
51 Ledbury Road Tel.229 6056
Silver, Sheffield plate, porcelain, paintings.

REX ANTIQUES
63 Ledbury Road Tel.229 6203
Furniture.

ROD'S ANTIQUES
82b Portobello Road Tel.229 2544
Barometers, copper, nautical items.

ROGERS ANTIQUE GALLERY
65 Portobello Road . . . . see page 29

G. SARTI ANTIQUES LTD.
186 Westbourne Grove Tel.221 7186
Furniture, fine art.

SHERATON ANTIQUES LTD.
192 Westbourne Grove Tel.229 8748
Furniture.

DAVID SLATER
170 Westbourne Grove Tel.727 3336
General antiques.

LOUIS STANTON
299 Westbourne Grove Tel.727 9336
Furniture, metalware, tapestries.

L. & M. SUTTON
91 Portobello Road Tel.727 0386
General antiques.

MURRAY THOMSON LTD.
233 Westbourne Grove Tel.221 8174
General antiques.

IGOR TOCIAPSKI
39-41 Ledbury Road Tel.229 8317
Clocks, scientific instruments.

TRUDE WEAVER
71 Portobello Road Tel.229 8738
Furniture, textiles.

A.M. WEB
93 Portobello Road Tel.727 1485
Musical boxes, toys.

THE WITCH BALL
206 Westbourne Grove Tel.229 3908
Victorian furniture.

WORLD FAMOUS PORTOBELLO MARKET
177 Portobello Road and 1-3 Elgin Crescent . . . . see page 29

W.13. Ealing

QUEST ANTIQUES
90 Northfield Avenue Tel.840 2349
Furniture.

W.13 ANTIQUES
10 The Avenue Tel.998 0390
General antiques.

W.14. West Kensington

R. & D. COOMBES
7 Charleville Road Tel.385 3785
Oriental works of art.

SIMPSON PINE MIRRORS
17 Girdlers Road Tel.603 8625
Pine mirrors.

S.W.1. Belgravia, Knightsbridge, St. James's, Victoria

DIDIER AARON (LONDON) LTD.
21 Ryder Street Tel.839 4716
18th C French furniture, paintings.

ADDISON-ROSS GALLERY
40 Eaton Terrace Tel.730 1536
Paintings, prints.

ALBANY GALLERY
1 Bury Street Tel.839 6119
18th-19th C watercolors, paintings.

J.A. ALLEN & CO.
1 Lower Grosvenor Place Tel.834 5606
Horse books.

S.W.1.

ALBERT AMOR LTD.
37 Bury Street....................Tel.930 2444
18th C porcelain, pottery.

ANNO DOMINO ANTIQUES
66 Pimlico Road....................Tel.730 5496
Furniture.

APPLEBY BROS. LTD.
8-10 Ryder Street....................Tel.930 2209
Paintings, watercolors.

ARTEMIS FINE ART (U.K.) LTD.
15 Duke Street....................Tel.930 1523
Paintings.

MAURICE ASPREY LTD.
41 Duke Street....................Tel.930 3921
Jewelry, silver, Sheffield plate.

ASTLEYS
109 Jermyn Street....................Tel.930 1687
Pipes, smoking accessories.

BAYLY'S GALLERY ANTIQUES
8 Prince's Arcade, Piccadilly....................Tel.734 0180
Porcelain, samplers, prints.

THOMAS BEAUMONT ANTIQUES LTD.
84 Pimlico Road....................Tel.730 1015
Biedermeier furniture.

CHRIS BEETLES LTD.
5 Ryder Street....................Tel.930 8586
Watercolors.

BELGRAVIA GALLERY
17 Lowndes Street....................Tel.235 4976
Oriental Art.

RAYMOND BENARDOUT
4 William Street....................Tel.235 3360
Carpets, rugs, furniture.

J.H. BOURDON-SMITH LTD.
24 Mason's Yard, Duke Street....................Tel.839 4714
Silver, Sheffield plate.

BOX HOUSE ANTIQUES
105 Pimlico Road....................Tel.730 9257
17th-19th C furniture, needlework.

CAMERER CUSS & CO.
17 Ryder Street....................Tel.930 1942
Clocks, watches.

CAVENDISH RARE BOOKS
2-4 Princes Arcade, Piccadilly....................Tel.734 3840
Antiquarian books-travel, voyages.

CHAUCER FINE ARTS INC.
45 Pimlico Road....................Tel.730 2972
Paintings, drawings.

CIANCIMINO LTD.
99 Pimlico Road Tel.730 9950
Oriental works of art.

MARY COOKE ANTIQUES
15 King Street Tel.839 6566
Silver.

CORNUCOPIA
12 Upper Tachbrook Street Tel.828 5752
Jewelry.

CRANE GALLERY
171a Sloane Street Tel.235 2464
Folk art, furniture, paintings.

CSAKY'S ANTIQUES
20 Pimlico Road Tel.730 2068
Oak furniture, works of art.

ARTHUR DAVIDSON LTD.
78-79 Jermyn Street Tel.930 6687
Scientfic instruments, furniture.

KENNETH DAVIS
38 Bury Street Tel.930 0313
Silver.

DE HAVILLAND (ANTIQUES) LTD.
48 Sloane Street Tel.235 3534
18th C furniture, silver, clocks.

DOUWES FINE ART
38 Duke Street Tel.839 5795
Paintings, watercolors, prints.

OWEN EDGAR GALLERY
9 West Halkin Street Tel.235 8989
Paintings.

M. EKSTEIN LTD.
90 Jermyn Street Tel.930 2024
Jewelry, porcelain, silver.

FERNANDES & MARCHE
23 Motcomb Street Tel.235 6773
18th C furniture, mirrors.

KATE FOSTER LTD.
9 Halkin Arcade, Motcomb Street Tel.245 9848
Porcelain, pottery.

S. FRANSES LTD.
82 Jermyn Street Tel.235 1888
Carpets, rugs, tapestries.

VICTOR FRANSES GALLERY
57 Jermyn Street Tel.493 6284
Carpets, rugs, tapestries.

FRY GALLERY
58 Jermyn Street Tel.493 4496
Watercolors, drawings.

ROBIN GAGE
50 Pimlico Road......................by appointment......................Tel.730 2878
Furniture, humidors.

GALLERY '25
4 Halkin Arcade, Motcomb Street......................Tel.235 5178
Furniture, art, glass.

GENERAL TRADING CO. LTD.
144 Sloane Street......................Tel.730 0411
Furniture, prints, porcelain, pewter.

ROSS HAMILTON
95 Pimlico Road......................Tel.730 3015
17th-19th C furniture, paintings.

CHARLES HAMMOND LTD.
165 Sloane Street......................Tel.235 2151
Furniture.

HARARI & JOHNS LTD.
12 Duke Street......................Tel.839 7671
Paintings.

HAZLITT, GOODEN & FOX LTD.
38 Bury Street......................Tel.930 6422
Paintings.

HEIM GALLERY
59 Jermyn Street......................Tel.493 0688
Paintings, sculpture.

HERAZ
25 Motcomb Street......................Tel.235 7416
Carpets, tapestries.

HERMITAGE ANTIQUES
97 Pimlico Road......................Tel.730 1973
Furniture.

CHRISTOPHER HODSOLL
69 Pimlico Road......................Tel.730 9835
Furniture, carpets, porcelain, paintings.

HOTSPUR LTD.
14 Lowndes Street......................Tel.235 1918
Furniture.

HOW OF EDINBURGH
2-3 Pickering Place......................Tel.930 7140
Silver.

ICONASTAS
5 Piccadilly Arcade......................Tel.629 1433
Icons.

BRAND INGLIS LTD.
9 Halkin Arcade, Motcomb Street......................Tel.235 6604
Silver, Sheffield plate.

ALAN JACOBS GALLERY
8 Duke Street......................Tel.930 3709
Paintings.

H.R. JESSOP LTD.
2-3 Pickering Place Tel.930 4696
Silver.

OSCAR & PETER JOHNSON LTD.
27 Lowndes Street Tel.235 6464
Paintings, prints.

DAVID KER FINE ART
85 Bourne Street Tel.730 3523
Watercolors, paintings, prints.

KING STREET GALLERIES
17 King Street Tel.930 3993
Paintings.

LANE FINE ART LTD.
86-88 Pimlico Road Tel.730 7374
Paintings.

LASSON GALLERY
34 Duke Street Tel.930 5950
Paintings.

LEGGATT BROTHERS
17 Duke Street Tel.930 3772
Paintings.

PAUL LONGMIRE LTD.
12 Bury Street Tel.930 8720
Jewelry, silver.

LOOT
76-78 Pimlico Road Tel.730 8097
Furniture.

MacCONNAL MASON GALLERY
14 Duke Street Tel.839 7693
Paintings, prints, drawings.

PAUL MASON
149 Sloane Street Tel.730 3683
Paintings, prints.

MATHAF GALLERY LTD.
24 Motcomb Street Tel.235 0010
Paintings.

MAYORCAS LTD.
38 Jermyn Street Tel.629 4195
Carpets, rugs, tapestries.

RICHARD MILES ANTIQUES
8 Holbein Place Tel.730 1957
Furniture, works of art.

LENNOX MONEY (ANTIQUES) LTD.
93 Pimlico Road Tel.730 3070
Furniture.

PETER NAHUM
5 Ryder Street Tel.930 6059
Paintings, bronzes.

OMEL GALLERIES
43 Duke Street....Tel.930 7744
Paintings.

O'SHEA GALLERY
89 Lower Sloane Street....Tel.730 0081
Prints, maps, books.

PAWSEY & PAYNE
4 Ryder Street....Tel.930 4221
Paintings, watercolors.

PICKERING & CHATTO LTD.
17 Pall Mall....Tel.930 2515
Antiquarian books-English literature, economics, science, medicine.

POLAK GALLERY
21 King Street....Tel.930 9245
Paintings.

PYMS GALLERY
13 Motcomb Street....Tel.235 3050
Paintings.

J.A. REDMILE LTD.
95 Pimlico Road....Tel.730 0557
Furniture.

GEOFFREY ROSE LTD.
77 Pimlico Road....Tel.730 3004
Furniture.

THOMAS E. SCHUSTER
9 Gillingham Street....Tel.828 7963
Prints, maps, books.

JOHN CARLTON SMITH
17 Ryder Street....Tel.930 6622
Clocks, barometers.

SPINK & SON LTD.
5-7 King Street....Tel.930 7888
Paintings, silver, jewelry, coins.

GERALD SPYER & SON (ANTIQUES) LTD.
18 Motcomb Street....Tel.235 3348
Furniture, bronzes.

ROBIN SYMES LTD.
94 Jermyn Street....Tel.930 5300
Antiquities.

TEMPUS ANTIQUES LTD.
2-4 King Street....Tel.839 5144
Oriental works of art.

TROVE
71 Pimlico Road....Tel.730 6514
Furniture, bronzes, paintings.

JOHNNY VAN HAEFTEN LTD.
13 Duke Street Tel.930 3062
Paintings.

DAVID WESTON LTD.
44 Duke Street Tel.839 1051
Scientific instruments.

WINIFRED WILLIAMS
3 Bury Street Tel.930 4732
Porcelain, enamels.

CHRISTOPHER WOOD GALLERY
15 Motcomb Street Tel.235 9141
Paintings, watercolors.

S.W.3. Chelsea Knightsbridge

NORMAN ADAMS LTD.
8-10 Hans Road Tel.589 5266
18th C furniture, glass, objets d'art.

MARIA ANDIPA
162 Walton Street Tel.589 2371
Icons.

ANTIQUARIUS ANTIQUE MARKET
135-141 King's Road . . . . see page 26

APTER FREDERICKS LTD.
265-267 Fulham Road Tel.352 2188
Furniture.

H.C. BAXTER & SONS
191-193 Fulham Road Tel.352 9826
Furniture.

JOANNA BOOTH
247 King's Road Tel.352 8998
Furniture, books, tapestries.

TONY BUNZL & ZAL DAVAR
344 King's Road Tel.352 3697
Furniture.

W.G.T. BURNE (ANTIQUE GLASS) LTD.
11 Elystan Street Tel.589 6074
Glass.

ANTIQUARIUS
135/141 Kings Rd. Chelsea London SW3
Open Monday to Saturday 10am to 6pm
Information from the Press Office 15 Flood Street London SW3 01-351 5353 Telex 894638

S.W.3.

JOHN CAMPBELL PICTURE FRAMES LTD.
164 Walton Street........Tel.584 9268
Prints, frames.

CHELSEA ANTIQUE MARKET
245a & 253 King's Road........see page 26

CHELSEA RARE BOOKS
313 King's Road........Tel.351 0950
Antiquarian books, maps, prints.

CHENIL GALLERIES
181-183 King's Road........see page 26

PHILIP COLLECK LTD.
84 Fulham Road........Tel.584 8479
Furniture.

RICHARD COURTNEY LTD.
112-114 Fulham Road........Tel.370 4020
Furniture.

ROBERT DICKSON ANTIQUES
263 Fulham Road........Tel.351 0330
Furniture.

MICHAEL FOSTER
118 Fulham Road........Tel.373 3636
Furniture.

Chelsea Antique Market

245/253 KINGS ROAD,
LONDON SW3
(opposite Carlyle Square)

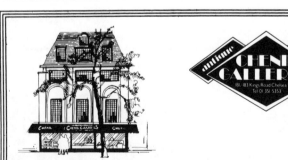

antique centre
CHENIL GALLERIES
181/183 Kings Road Chelsea SW3
Tel 01 351 5353

181/183 Kings Rd. Chelsea
London SW3
Open Monday to Saturday
10am to 6pm

C. FREDERICKS & SON
92 Fulham Road........Tel.589 5847
Furniture.

STEPHEN GARRATT (FINE PAINTINGS)
146 Brompton Road........Tel.603 0861
Paintings.

GODSON & COLES
310 King's Road........Tel.352 8509
Furniture.

HALLIDAY'S (ANTIQUES) LTD.
28 Beauchamp Place........Tel.589 5534
Mantelpieces, grates.

MICHAEL HOGG ANTIQUES
172 Brompton Road........Tel.589 8629
Furniture, Chinese porcelain.

E. HOLLANDER LTD.
80 Fulham Road........Tel.589 7239
Clocks, barometers, silver.

HOOPER & PURCHASE
303 King's Road........Tel.351 3985
Furniture.

STEPHANIE HOPPEN LTD.
17 Walton Street........Tel.589 3678
Prints

ANTHONY JAMES & SON LTD.
88 Fulham Road........Tel.584 1120
Furniture, bronzes.

DAVID JAMES FINE PAINTINGS
291 Brompton Road........Tel.581 3399
Victorian watercolors.

JEREMY LTD.
255 King's Road........Tel.352 3127
Furniture.

LEWIS M. KAPLAN ASSOCIATES LTD.
50 Fulham Road........Tel.589 3108
Art Deco & Art Nouveau furniture, glass, jewelry.

JOHN KEIL LTD.
154 Brompton Road........Tel.589 6454
Furniture.

LEDGER ANTIQUES LTD.
101a Fulham Road........Tel.581 0922
Pottery.

STANLEY LESLIE
15 Beauchamp Place........Tel.589 2333
Silver, Sheffield plate.

MICHAEL LIPITCH
98 Fulham Road........Tel.589 7327
Furniture.

S.W.3.

PETER LIPITCH LTD.
120-124 Fulham Road Tel.373 3328
Furniture.

THE MAP HOUSE
54 Beauchamp Place Tel.589 4325
Maps, globes, engravings.

H.W. NEWBY
15 Walton Street Tel.589 2752
Glass, pottery, porcelain.

PELHAM GALLERIES
163-165 Fulham Road Tel.589 2686
Furniture, tapestries, clocks.

DAVID PETTIFER LTD.
269 King's Road Tel.352 3088
Furniture.

ALISTAIR SAMPSON ANTIQUES
156 Brompton Road Tel.589 5272
Furniture, metalware, pottery.

LOUISE STROUD F.G.A.
3 Cale Street, Chelsea Green Tel.351 5988
Jewelry.

TEMPLE GALLERY
4 Yeoman's Row Tel.589 6622
Icons.

DAVID TREMAYNE LTD.
320 King's Road Tel.352 1194
Furniture, Oriental works of art.

DAVID TRON ANTIQUES
275 King's Road Tel.352 5918
Furniture.

EARLE D. VANDEKAR OF KNIGHTSBRIDGE LTD.
138 Brompton Road Tel.589 8481
Glass, porcelain, pottery.

R. WEARN & SON LTD.
322 King's Road Tel.352 3918
General antiques.

O.F. WILSON LTD.
3-6 Queens Elm Parade, Old Church Street Tel.352 9554
Furniture, mantelpieces.

CLIFFORD WRIGHT ANTIQUES LTD.
104-106 Fulham Road Tel.589 0986
Furniture, mirrors.

S.W.5. Earl's Court

KENWAY ANTIQUES
70 Kenway Road Tel.373 1631
General antiques.

SANDA LIPTON
35 Kenway Road Tel.373 9625
Silver, flatware.

S.W.6. Fulham

ADAMS ANTIQUES
53-55 Fulham Road Tel.736 9136
Pine furniture.

GIL ADAMS ANTIQUES
659 Fulham Road Tel.731 7372
General antiques.

DAVID ALEXANDER ANTIQUES
102 Waterford Road Tel.731 4644
Furniture, Chinese works of art.

AND SO TO BED LTD.
638-640 King's Road Tel.731 3593
Beds.

ANVIL INTERIORS
55 New King's Road Tel.736 5623
Pine furniture.

KARIN ARMELIN ANTIQUES
594 New King's Road Tel.736 0375
18th-19th C furniture, silver

ATLANTIC BAY CARPETS
739 Fulham Road Tel.736 8777
Carpets.

AUBYN ANTIQUES
1 Wandon Road Tel.736 1196
Furniture, watercolors, prints.

ROBERT BARLEY ANTIQUES
48 Fulham High Street Tel.736 4429
Furniture.

BERESFORD-CLARK
558 King's Road Tel.731 5079
Furniture, china, paintings.

BIG BEN ANTIQUE CLOCKS
5 Broxholme House, New King's Road Tel.736 1770
Clocks, watches.

R. BONNETT
582 King's Road Tel.736 4593
Furniture.

BOOKHAM GALLERIES
164 Wandsworth Bridge Road Tel.736 5125
Furniture, rugs.

I. & J.L. BROWN
636 King's Road Tel.736 4141
Furniture, metalware.

C.W. BUCKINGHAM
301-303 Munster Road Tel.385 2657
Pine furniture, Windsor chairs.

RUPERT CAVENDISH ANTIQUES
561 King's Road Tel.731 7041
Furniture, watercolors, paintings.

CHELSEA CLOCKS & ANTIQUES
479 Fulham Road Tel.731 5704
Clocks.

JOHN CLAY
263 New King's Road Tel.731 5677
Furniture, silver, clocks.

FERGUS COCHRANE ANTIQUES
570 King's Road Tel.736 9166
Furniture.

T. CROWTHER & SON LTD.
282 North End Road Tel.385 1375
Furniture, chimney pieces, panelling.

ROCCO D'ALESSANDRO
610 King's Road Tel.731 7160
Furniture.

ZAL DAVAR ANTIQUES
26a Munster Road Tel.736 2559
Furniture, barometers.

PETER EVANSON
464 Fulham Road Tel.385 4185
General antiques.

FIVE FIVE SIX ANTIQUES
556 King's Road Tel.731 2016
Furniture, paintings.

FLEUR DE LYS GALLERY
8 Fulham High Street Tel.731 7454
Paintings, watercolors.

JUDY GREENWOOD ANTIQUES

657 FULHAM ROAD · LONDON SW6 5PY · TEL: 01-736 6037

19th C textiles, quilts, paisleys.
Decorative & country antiques.

GEORGE FLOYD LTD.
592 Fulham Road Tel.736 1649
Furniture.

IMOGEN GRAHAM
585 King's Road Tel.736 2465
Furniture, paintings.

ALEX GRAHAMSLAW
583 King's Road Tel.731 1245
Furniture, objets d'art.

JUDY GREENWOOD ANTIQUES
657 Fulham Road Tel.736 6037
Textiles, quilts, paisleys, country antiques.

GUINEVERE ANTIQUES
574-580 King's Road Tel.736 2917
General antiques.

HOLLINGSHEAD & CO.
783 Fulham Road Tel.385 8519
Mantelpieces, grates, fenders.

JUST A SECOND ANTIQUES LTD.
40 Fulham High Street Tel.731 1919
Furniture, silver, china.

ERIC KING ANTIQUES
203 New King's Road Tel.736 3162
Furniture.

M. LASSOTA
596 King's Road Tel.736 3932
Furniture.

LILLIE ANTIQUES
244-246 Lillie Road Tel.385 9852
Furniture, paintings.

LUNN ANTIQUES
86 New King's Road Tel.736 4638
Linens.

MICHAEL MARRIOTT LTD.
588 Fulham Road Tel.736 3110
Furniture.

IAN MOGGACH ANTIQUES
723 Fulham Road Tel.731 4883
Furniture.

RICHARD MORRIS ANTIQUES
142 Wandsworth Bridge Road Tel.736 1448
Pine furniture.

OLD WORLD TRADING CO.
565 King's Road Tel.731 4708
Furniture.

PAISNEL GALLERY LTD.
768 Fulham Road Tel.736 7898
Paintings, watercolors.

THE PINE MINE
96 & 100 Wandsworth Bridge Road....Tel.736 1092
Pine furniture.

THE PINE VILLAGE
162 Wandsworth Bridge Road....Tel.736 2753
Pine furniture.

BARRIE QUINN ANTIQUES
3 & 4 Broxholme House, New King's Road....Tel.736 4747
General antiques.

RENDALL ANTIQUES
572 King's Road....Tel.736 2520
Furniture.

SIMON LEIGH ROSE
569 King's Road....Tel.731 7356
Furniture.

PATRICK SANDBERG ANTIQUES
791 Fulham Road....Tel.736 9454
General antiques.

SAVILE PINE
560 King's Road....Tel.736 3625
Pine furniture.

SENSATION LTD.
66 Fulham High Street....Tel.736 4135
Furniture, porcelain, pottery, silver.

DAVID SEYFRIED ANTIQUES
759 Fulham Road....Tel.731 4230
Furniture, ceramics, prints.

GEORGE SHERLOCK
588-589 King's Road....Tel.736 3955
General antiques.

SHIELD & ALLEN ANTIQUES
584-586 King's Road....Tel.736 7145
Furniture, paintings.

THORNHILL GALLERIES LTD.
76 New King's Road....Tel.736 5830
Chimney pieces, panelled rooms, fenders.

THROUGH THE LOOKING GLASS LTD.
563 King's Road....Tel.736 7799
Mirrors.

LEIGH WARREN ANTIQUES
566 King's Road....Tel.736 2485
General antiques.

CHRISTOPHER WRAY'S LIGHTING EMPORIUM
600-604 King's Road....Tel.736 8434
Light fittings.

S.W.7. Knightsbridge, South Kensington

ANGLO-PERSIAN CARPET CO. LTD.
6 Sth. Kensington Station Arcade.......Tel.589 5457
Carpets, rugs.

BENARDOUT & BENARDOUT
7 Thurloe Place.......Tel.584 7658
Carpets, rugs, tapestries.

AUBREY BROCKLEHURST
124 Cromwell Road.......Tel.373 0319
Clocks, barometers.

M.P. LEVENE LTD.
5 Thurloe Place.......Tel.589 3755
Silver, Sheffield plate.

MICHAEL & MARGARET PARKER ANTIQUES
24 Cheval Place.......Tel.589 0133
Furniture.

JOHN POPE & HUNTS LTD.
91 Old Brompton Road.......Tel.581 5375
Furniture, clocks.

S.W.8. Battersea

NICHOLAS BEECH
787 Wandsworth Road.......Tel.720 8552
Pine furniture.

CAPITAL CLOCKS
190 Wandsworth Road.......Tel.720 6372
Clocks.

S.W.10 West Brompton

CHANTEAU
36 Cathcart Road.......Tel.352 0447
General antiques.

FURNITURE CAVE
533 King's Road.......Tel.352 2046
Furniture.

WILLIAM HANDFORD ANTIQUES
517 King's Road.......Tel.351 2768
General antiques.

CARLTON HOBBS
533 King's Road.......Tel.351 3870
Furniture.

H.W. POULTER & SON
279 Fulham Road.......Tel.352 7268
Chimney pieces, fenders, chandeliers.

RENDLESHAM & DARK
498 King's Road.......Tel.351 1442
Furniture, objets d'art.

S.W.10.

HARRIET WYNTER LTD.
50 Redcliffe Road .... by appointment Tel.352 6494
Scientific instruments.

S.W.11. Battersea, Clapham

CHRISTOPHER BANGS
By appointment only Tel.223 5676
Metalware, works of art.

TONY DAVIS INC.
235-239 Lavender Hill Tel.228 1370
Furniture, glass, china.

ROBERT YOUNG ANTIQUES
68 Battersea Bridge Road Tel.228 7847
Furniture, metalware, pottery.

S.W.13. Barnes

BEVERLEY BROOK ANTIQUES
29 Grove Road Tel.878 5656
General antiques.

SIMON COLEMAN ANTIQUES
40 White Hart Lane Tel.878 5037
Country furniture.

GOTHIC COTTAGE ANTIQUES
70 Station Road Tel.876 2026
Pine furniture.

JOHN HAINES ANTIQUES LTD.
59 Elm Grove Road .... by appointment Tel.876 4215
Furniture, metalware.

JOY McDONALD
50 Station Road Tel.876 6184
Furniture, metalware.

PORTMEIRION ANTIQUES
62 White Hart Lane Tel.876 2367
General antiques.

RANDALLS ANTIQUES
46-52 Church Road Tel.748 1858
General antiques.

REMEMBER WHEN
7 Rocks Lane Tel.878 2817
Pine Furniture.

S.W.14. East Sheen, Mortlake

DIXON'S ANTIQUE MARKET
471 Upper Richmond Road West .... see page 28

S.W.14.

HELIUS ANTIQUES
487-493 Upper Richmond Road West....................................Tel.876 5721
General antiques. Trade only.

MORTLAKE ANTIQUES
69 Lower Richmond Road....................................Tel.876 8715
Furniture, clocks.

VANDELEUR ANTIQUARIAN BOOKS
69 Sheen Lane....................................Tel.878 6837
Antiquarian books, prints, maps.

S.W.15. Putney

R.A. BARNES ANTIQUES
26 Lower Richmond Road....................................Tel.789 3371
General antiques.

J. & R. BATEMAN ANTIQUES
12 Lower Richmond Road....................................Tel.789 3124
Country furniture.

SUSAN BECKER ANTIQUES
18 Lower Richmond Road....................................Tel.788 9082
Porcelain.

THE CLOCK CLINIC LTD.
85 Lower Richmond Road....................................Tel.788 1407
Clocks.

CREST ANTIQUES
313-315 Putney Bridge Road....................................Tel.789 3165
General antiques.

FOSTER OF PUTNEY
146 Upper Richmond Road....................................Tel.373 5135
General antiques.

JORGEN ANTIQUES
40 Lower Richmond Road....................................Tel.789 7329
Furniture.

MICHAEL PHELPS
19 Chelverton Road....................................Tel.785 6766
Antiquarian books.

ALAN STONE ANTIQUES
3 Wadham Road....................................Tel.870 1606
General antiques.

THORNHILL GALLERIES LTD.
78 Deodar Road....................................Tel.874 2101
Chimney pieces, fenders, panelled rooms.

VAUGHAN
75 Lower Richmond Road....................................Tel.789 4245
General antiques.

S.W.16. Streatham

S. FARRELLY
634 Streatham High Road........Tel.764 4028
General antiques.

A. & J. FOWLE
542 Streatham High Road........Tel.764 2896
General antiques.

STREATHAM TRADERS & SHIPPERS MARKET
United Reform Church Hall........see page 29

S.W.19. Wimbledon

ADAMS ROOM ANTIQUES
18-20 Ridgway, Wimbledon Village........Tel.946 7047
General antiques.

CHELSEA BRIC-A-BRAC SHOP LTD.
16 Hartfield Road........Tel.946 6894
General antiques.

CLUNES ANTIQUES
9 West Place, Wimbledon Common........Tel.946 1643
General antiques, Staffordshire figures, theatricalia.

J.F. EWING
11 High Street, Wimbledon Village........Tel.946 4700
Jewelry, silver.

THE LIGHTHOUSE LTD.
67 Ridgway........Tel.946 2050
Chandeliers, small furniture.

RICHARD MARYAN & DAUGHTERS
177 Merton Road........Tel.542 5846
General antiques.

MARK J. WEST - COBB ANTIQUES LTD.
39b High Street, Wimbledon Village........Tel.946 2811
18th-19th C table glass.

WIMBLEDON PINE CO.
264 Haydons Road........Tel.540 5032
Pine furniture.

S.W.20. Raynes Park

DEN OF ANTIQUITY
96 Coombe Lane........Tel.947 0850
General antiques.

S.E.1. Southwark

THE ANTIQUES EXCHANGE
1 Bermondsey Square........Tel.407 3635
Small items.

S.E.1.

BERMONDSEY ANTIQUE MARKET
Bermondsey Street/Long Lane . . . . see page 26

BERMONDSEY ANTIQUE WAREHOUSE
173 Bermondsey Street Tel.407 2040
General antiques-7 dealers.

BERMONDSEY ANTIQUES
245 Long Lane Tel.407 0309
General antiques. Trade only.

LAMONT ANTIQUES LTD.
151 Tower Bridge Road Tel.403 0126
Architectural items, furniture.

MacNEILL'S ART & ANTIQUE WAREHOUSE
175 Bermondsey Street Tel.403 0022
Furniture.

OOLA BOOLA ANTIQUES
166 Tower Bridge Road Tel.403 0749
Furniture.

PENNY FARTHING ANTIQUES ARCADE
177 Bermondsey Street Tel.407 5171
General antiques.

TOWER BRIDGE ANTIQUE WAREHOUSE LTD.
163 Tower Bridge Road Tel.403 3660
Furniture, clocks, porcelain.

S.E.5. Camberwell

FRANKLIN'S CAMBERWELL ANTIQUES MARKET
161 Camberwell Road . . . . see page 28

SCALLYWAG
The Old Church, Wren Road Tel.701 5353
Pine furniture.

S.E.6. Catford

SILVER SIXPENCE
14 Catford Hill Tel.690 0046
Pine furniture, clocks.

Bermondsey antique market
& Open Friday mornings 5am to 2pm
Antique Hypermarket
Open Monday to Friday
On the corner of
Long Lane and
Bermondsey St.
London SE1 01-351 5353 Telex 894638

S.E.10. Greenwich

THE GREEN PARROT
2 Turnpin Lane Tel.858 6690
Porcelain, small furniture.

GREENWICH ANTIQUES MARKET
Greenwich High Road . . . . see page 28

GREENWICH CHIMES
11 Nelson Road Tel.858 3706
General antiques.

A. POLLY
8 Turnpin Lane Tel.858 4048
Furniture, clocks.

RELCY ANTIQUES
9 Nelson Road Tel.858 2812
Furniture, marine items.

ROGERS TURNER BOOKS LTD.
22 Nelson Road Tel.853 5271
Antiquarian books - Horology, scientific instruments.

SPREAD EAGLE ANTIQUES
23 Nelson Road Tel.858 9713
General antiques.

RUSSELL WOOD ANTIQUES
20 Greenwich Church Street Tel.853 0200
General antiques.

S.E.13. Lewisham

ACTINO ANTIQUES
136 Lee High Road Tel.318 1273
Furniture, fenders.

RIVERDALE HALL ANTIQUE MARKET
Lewisham Centre, Rennell Street . . . . see page 29

WHITWORTH & O'DONNELL LTD.
282 Lewisham High Street Tel.690 1282
Jewelry.

S.E.15. Peckham

PETER ALLEN ANTIQUES LTD.
17 Nunhead Green Tel.732 1968
Furniture.

THE ANTIQUE GALLERY
40 Peckham Rye Tel.732 7808
Furniture, metalware, clocks.

S.E.15.

G. AUSTIN & SONS LTD.
39-41 Brayards Road Tel.639 0480
11-23 Peckham Rye Tel.639 3163
Furniture, silver, porcelain, pictures.

BUTCHOFF ANTIQUES
48 Peckham Rye Tel.639 0736
Furniture.

A.J. MANGION ANTIQUES
1a Philip Walk Tel.732 6749
Furniture.

PECKHAM RYE ANTIQUES
80 Peckham Rye Tel.639 9723
Furniture.

WAVENEY ANTIQUES
58 & 68 Peckham Rye Tel.732 1251
General antiques.

IAN WILSON ANTIQUES
70-72 Peckham Rye Tel.639 5068
Furniture.

S.E.18. Plumstead

LAWRENCE ANTIQUES
70 Plumstead High Street Tel.854 2380
Furniture, metalware.

S.E.21. West Dulwich

ACORN ANTIQUES
111 Rosendale Road Tel.761 3349
General antiques.

S.E.26. Sydenham

OLWEN CARTHEW
109 Kirkdale Tel.699 1363
Country furniture.

DENTON ANTIQUES
133 Kirkdale Tel.291 2123
General antiques.

HILLYERS
301 Sydenham Road Tel.778 6361
General antiques.

VINTAGE CAMERAS LTD.
254-256 Kirkdale Tel.778 5416
Cameras, scientific instruments.

E.1. Whitechapel

CUTLER STREET ANTIQUE MARKET
Goulston Street. . . . . see page 28

E.17. Walthamstow

ANTIQUE CITY
98 Wood Street. Tel.520 4032
General antiques. Trade only.

GEORGIAN VILLAGE ANTIQUES MARKET
100 Wood Street. Tel.520 6638
General antiques-10 dealers.

J.C. ANTIQUES
12 Warwick Terrace, Lea Bridge Road. Tel.539 4275
Furniture. Trade only.

E.C.1. Holborn

ELDRIDGE LONDON & CO.
99-101 Farringdon Road. Tel.837 0379
Furniture, decorative items.

ESSIE C. HARRIS
Diamond House, 63-66 Hatton Garden. Tel.242 9115
Jewelry.

HOUSE OF BUCKINGHAM ANTIQUES
113-117 Farringdon Road. Tel.276 2013
Furniture, clocks, brass.

THE
CITY OF LONDON
ANTIQUES FAIR

The Barbican Exhibition Centre
100 stands, high quality
most items pre-1870

NOVEMBER 24~28

Enquiries:
P.O. Box 114
Haywards Heath, W. Sussex
Tel: 04447–2514

Penman Antiques Fairs

E.C.1.

OLD STREET ANTIQUES
64 Old Street ... Tel.235 1342
Furniture.

PRIORY ANTIQUES
45 Cloth Fair, West Smithfield ... Tel.606 9060
Jewelry.

A.R. ULLMANN LTD.
10 Hatton Garden ... Tel.405 1877
Jewelry, silver.

C.J. VANDER (ANTIQUES) LTD.
Dunstan House, 14a St. Cross Street ... Tel.831 6741
Silver, Sheffield plate. Trade only.

E.C.3. City of London

ASPREY & CO. (CITY BRANCH) LTD.
153 Fenchurch Street ... Tel.626 2160
Silver, jewelry, clocks.

HALCYON DAYS
4 Royal Exchange ... Tel.629 8811
Georgian enamels, papier mâché, tole prints.

ROYAL EXCHANGE ART GALLERY
14 Royal Exchange ... Tel.283 4400
Paintings, watercolors.

SEARLE & CO. LTD.
1 Royal Exchange ... Tel.626 2456
Silver, jewelry.

W.C.1. Bloomsbury

CARTOGRAPHIA LTD.
Pied Bull Yard, Bury Place ... Tel.240 5687
15th-19th C maps, engravings.

Cartographia
limited

Pied Bull Yard
Bury Place
Bloomsbury, London W.C.1.

Telephone: 01-240 5687

Original Maps & Engravings

W.C.1.

PETER FRANCIS
26 Museum Street........Tel.637 0165
Furniture, porcelain.

J.I. HORWIT
94 Southampton Row........Tel.405 0749
Jewelry.

THE PRINT ROOM
37 Museum Street........Tel.430 0159
Antiquarian books, prints.

SHAPLAND
207 High Holborn........Tel.405 3507
Silver, jewelry.

S.J. SHRUBSOLE LTD.
43 Museum Street........Tel.405 2712
Silver, Sheffield plate.

SKOOB BOOKS LTD.
15 Sicilian Avenue........Tel.404 3063
Antiquarian books.

W.C.2. Holborn, Strand

ANGLEBOOKS LTD.
2 Cecil Court, Charing Cross Road........Tel.836 2922
Antiquarian books.

A.H. BALDWIN & SONS LTD.
11 Adelphi Terrace........Tel.930 6879
Coins, medals.

CLIVE A. BURDEN LTD.
13 Cecil Court, Charing Cross Road........Tel.836 2177
Antiquarian books, maps, prints.

COVENT GARDEN FLEA MARKET
Jubilee Market........see page 28

THE DOLLS HOUSE TOYS LTD.
29 The Market, Covent Garden........Tel.379 7243
Dolls' houses, furniture.

ROBERT DOUWMA LTD.
4 Henrietta Street........Tel.836 0771
Maps, engravings.

H.M. FLETCHER
27 Cecil Court, Charing Cross Road........Tel.836 2865
Antiquarian books.

FROGNAL RARE BOOKS
18 Cecil Court, Charing Cross Road........Tel.240 2815
Antiquarian books.

GROSVENOR PRINTS
28-32 Shelton Street........Tel.836 1979
Prints.

S. & H. JEWELL
26 Parker Street Tel.405 8520
Furniture.

LANGFORDS GALLERIES
46 Chancery Lane Tel.405 6402
Scientific & marine items, silver.

THE LONDON SILVER VAULTS
53-65 Chancery Lane . . . . see page 28

ARTHUR MIDDLETON LTD.
12 New Row, Covent Garden Tel.836 7042
Scientific instruments.

W.A. MYERS (AUTOGRAPHS) LTD.
Suite 52,91 St. Martin's Lane Tel.836 1940
Autograph letters, manuscripts.

AVRIL NOBLE
2 Southampton Street Tel.240 1970
16th-19th C maps, engravings.

OLD CURIOSITY SHOP
13-14 Portsmouth Street Tel.405 9891
General antiques.

PEARL CROSS LTD.
35 St. Martin's Court Tel.836 2814
Jewelry, silver, clocks.

H. PEROVETZ LTD.
50-52 Chancery Lane Tel.405 8868
Silver, Sheffield plate.

REG & PHILIP REMINGTON
14 Cecil Court, Charing Cross Road Tel.836 9771
Antiquarian books.

BERTRAM ROTA LTD.
30-31 Long Acre Tel.836 0723
Antiquarian books.

THE SILVER MOUSE TRAP
56 Carey Street Tel.405 2578
Silver, Jewelry.

HAROLD T. STOREY
3 Cecil Court, Charing Cross Road Tel.836 3777
Antiquarian books, engravings.

N.1. Islington

THE ANTIQUE TRADER
357 Upper Street Tel.359 2019
Furniture, decorative items.

ARCHITECTURAL ANTIQUES LTD.
133 Upper Street Tel.226 5565
Architectural fittings.

WILLIAM BEDFORD ANTIQUES LTD.
The Merchants Hall, 46 Essex Road....Tel.226 9648
Fine furniture and works of art.

JOHN BIRCHMORE
23-25 Essex Road....Tel.226 8011
General antiques.

BUCK & PAYNE ANTIQUES
5 Camden Passage....Tel.226 4326
Country furniture, decorative items.

BUSHE ANTIQUES
52-53 Camden Passage....Tel.226 7096
Clocks.

BUSHWOOD ANTIQUES
317 Upper Street....Tel.359 2095
Furniture, clocks, porcelain, bronzes. Trade Only.

CAMDEN PASSAGE ANTIQUES CENTRE
357 Upper Street....see page 26

CANONBURY ANTIQUES
13 Canonbury Place....Tel.359 2246
General antiques.

PATRIC CAPON
350 Upper Street....Tel.354 0487
Clocks, barometers.

CAPRICORN ANTIQUES
76 Upper Street....Tel.226 4052
General antiques.

CHANCERY ANTIQUES LTD.
357a Upper Street....Tel.359 9035
Porcelain, Japenese works of art.

CHAPMAN & DAVIES ANTIQUES
10 Theberton Street....Tel.226 5565
Furniture, paintings.

JOHN CREED ANTIQUES LTD.
3 & 5a Camden Passage....Tel.226 8867
Furniture, metalware, china.

DOME ANTIQUES (EXPORTS) LTD.
75 Upper Street....Tel.226 7227
Furniture.

DONAY ANTIQUES
35 Camden Passage....Tel.359 1880
Furniture, textiles, games.

D.J. FERRANT ANTIQUES
21a Camden Passage....Tel.359 2597
General antiques.

THE FLEAMARKET
7 Pierrepont, Row, Camden Passage....Tel.226 8211
General antiques.

FRANCO'S ANTIQUE WAREHOUSE
69 Upper Street. Tel.226 7261
Furniture.

VINCENT FREEMAN
1 Camden Passage. Tel.226 6178
Glass, porcelain, music boxes.

FURNITURE VAULT
50 Camden Passage. Tel.354 1047
Furniture, clocks, bronzes.

GEORGIAN VILLAGE
Islington Green. . . . . see page 28

GERANIUM
121 Upper Street. Tel.359 4281
Pine furniture.

GORDON GRIDLEY
41 Camden Passage. Tel.226 0643
Furniture, metalware, paintings.

HART & ROSENBERG
2-3 Gateway Arcade, 355 Upper Street. Tel.359 6839
Oriental works of art.

SHEILA HART ANTIQUES
104 Islington High Street. Tel.226 2315
Furniture, decorative items.

BRIAN HAWKINS ANTIQUES
73 Upper Street. Tel.359 3957
Furniture.

HEATHER ANTIQUES
11 Camden Passage. Tel.226 2412
Silver.

HERITAGE ANTIQUES
112 Islington High Street. Tel.226 7789
Metalware, oak furniture.

INHERITANCE
98 Islington High Street. Tel.226 8305
Jewelry, ceramics, furniture, clocks.

JAPANESE GALLERY
23 Camden Passage. Tel.226 3347
Japanese antiques.

KAUSMALLY ANTIQUES
15 Islington Green. Tel.359 0741
Furniture.

THOMAS KERR ANTIQUES LTD.
11 Theberton Street. Tel.226 0626
Furniture, clocks, paintings.

JOHN LAURIE ANTIQUES LTD.
352 Upper Street. Tel.226 0913
Silver, Sheffield plate.

MICHAEL LEWIS ANTIQUES
16 Essex Road Tel.359 7733
Pine furniture.

WAN LI
7 Gateway Arcade Tel.226 0997
Chinese works of art.

THE MALL ANTIQUES ARCADE
359 Upper Street . . . . . see page 28

LAURENCE MITCHELL ANTIQUES
27 Camden Passage Tel.359 7579
Ceramics, glass, small furniture.

STEPHEN ORTON ANTIQUES
73 Upper Street Tel.226 2770
Furniture.

KEVIN A. PAGE ANTIQUES
5 Camden Passage Tel.226 8558
Furniture, porcelain, bronzes.

THE PERSIAN MARKET
48 Upper Street Tel.226 7927
Furniture, carpets, silver, porcelain.

THE SHOP ON THE CORNER
12 Camden Passage Tel.226 2444
Pine furniture, general antiques.

ROBIN SIMS
7 Camden Passage Tel.226 2393
General antiques.

KEITH SKEEL ANTIQUES
94 Islington High Street Tel.359 9894
Furniture, paintings, bronzes. Trade only.

STRIKE ONE(ISLINGTON) LTD.
51 Camden Passage Tel.226 9709
Clocks, barometers.

SWAN FINE ART
120 Islington High Street Tel.226 5335
Paintings, furniture.

LEIGH UNDERHILL GALLERY
100 Islington High Street Tel.226 5673
Paintings, sculpture.

VANE HOUSE ANTIQUES
15 Camden Passage Tel.359 1343
18th-19th C furniture.

G.W. WALFORD
186 Upper Street Tel.226 5682
Antiquarian books.

MARK J. WEST - COBB ANTIQUES LTD.
15 Georgian Village, Camden Passage Tel.359 8686
18th-19th C glass.

N.1.

YESTERDAY CHILD
24 The Mall, Camden Passage..Tel.354 1601
Dolls.

N.2. East Finchley

THE ANTIQUE SHOP
9 Fortis Green..Tel.883 7651
General antiques.

MARTIN HENHAM (ANTIQUES)
218 High Road..Tel.444 5274
Furniture, porcelain, paintings.

LAURI STEWART - FINE ART
36 Church Lane..Tel.883 7719
Paintings, watercolors.

N.3. Finchley

PARK GALLERIES
20 Hendon Lane..Tel.346 2176
Paintings, watercolors, prints.

N.4. Crouch Hill

MARION GRAY
33 Crouch Hill..Tel.272 0372
Furniture, objets d'art.

N.5. Highbury

TONY ELLIS ANTIQUES
90,96 & 100 Highbury Park..Tel.226 7551
Furniture.

ESTER ANTIQUES
88 Highbury Park..Tel.359 1573
General antiques.

NORTH LONDON CLOCK SHOP
72 Highbury Park..Tel.226 1609
Clocks.

N.6. Highgate

JOHN BEER
191-199 Archway Road..Tel.340 2183
Furniture.

N.6.

CENTAUR GALLERY
82 Highgate High Street.......Tel.340 0087
Paintings, watercolors, sculpture.

HIGHGATE GALLERY
26 Highgate High Street.......Tel.340 7564
Watercolors, pottery.

STUART MARTIN
355c Archway Road.......Tel.340 8354
Furniture.

N.7. Holloway

KEITH HARDING ANTIQUES
93 Hornsey Road.......Tel.607 6181
Clocks, musical boxes, books.

PRINCEDALE ANTIQUES
56 Eden Grove.......Tel.727 0868
Pine furniture, decorative items.

N.12. North Finchley

FINCHLEY FINE ART GALLERIES
983 High Road.......Tel.446 4848
General antiques.

N.19. Upper Holloway

TERRY ANTIQUES
175 Junction Road, Archway.......Tel.263 1219
18th-19th C furniture.

N.20. Whetstone

BARNET ANTIQUES & FINE ART
1180 High Road, Whetstone.......Tel.445 9695
Furniture, porcelain, pictures.

N.21. Southgate, Winchmore Hill

THE LITTLE CURIOSITY SHOP
24 The Green.......Tel.886 0925
General antiques. Trade only.

ROCHEFORT ANTIQUES GALLERY
32-34 The Green.......Tel.886 4779
General antiques-12 dealers.

N.W.1. Camden Town, Regent's Park

ADAMS ANTIQUES
47 Chalk Farm Road Tel.267 9241
Pine furniture.

B.P. ANTIQUES
2a Ferdinand Place Tel.482 4021
Furniture, clocks, barometers, paintings.

CAMDEN ANTIQUES TRADE MARKET
Camden High Street . . . . see page 26

THE CAMDEN LOCK ANTIQUES CENTRE
248 Camden High Street Tel.485 8072
General antiques-9 dealers.

COUNTRY PINE
13 Chalk Farm Road Tel.485 9687
Pine furniture.

IAN CRISPIN ANTIQUES
95 Lisson Grove Tel.402 6845
Shipping goods. Trade only.

GALERIE 1900
267 Camden High Street Tel.485 1001
Silver, jewelry, metalware, pottery, glass.

W.R. HARVEY & CO. (ANTIQUES) LTD.
67-70 Chalk Farm Road Tel.485 1504
Clocks, barometers, furniture.

CHAS L. NYMAN & CO. LTD.
230 & 242 Camden High Street Tel.485 1907
Furniture, porcelain. Trade only.

THE OLD STABLES MARKET
Stanley Sidings, Chalk Farm Road . . . . see page 29

REGENT ANTIQUES
9-10 Chester Court, Albany Street Tel.935 6944
Furniture, decorative items. Trade only.

W. TAUBER
94 Park Road Tel.723 6143
General antiques.

THIS AND THAT
50-51 Chalk Farm Road Tel.267 5433
Country furniture.

N.W.2. Cricklewood

THE CORNER CUPBOARD
679 Finchley Road Tel.435 4870
Jewelry, silver, china, glass.

N.W.3. Hampstead

PATRICIA BECKMAN ANTIQUES
10a Heath Drive . . . . by appointment Tel.435 5050
Furniture.

N.W.3.

TONY BINGHAM
11 Pond Street....Tel.794 1596
Musical instruments, books, manuscripts.

MICHAEL CARLETON
77-81 Haverstock Hill....Tel.722 2277
Furniture, paintings, watercolors.

S.A. COOK & SON
279 Finchley Road....Tel.435 4543
Furniture, silver.

CLIVE DANIEL ANTIQUES
91a Heath Street....Tel.435 4351
Furniture.

STEPHEN FARRELLY
152 Fleet Road....Tel.485 2089
General antiques.

OTTO HAAS
49 Belsize Park Gardens....Tel.722 1488
Manuscripts, autographs.

HAMPSTEAD ANTIQUE EMPORIUM
12 Heath Street....see page 28

HAVERSTOCK ANTIQUES
78 Haverstock Hill....Tel.267 1627
Furniture.

JUST DESKS
6 Erskine Road....Tel.723 7976
Desks, bureaux, chairs.

N.W.4. Hendon

ANTIQUES (HENDON) LTD.
18 Parson Street....Tel.203 1194
Furniture, paintings, china.

N.W.5. Kentish Town

M.E. KORN
51 Lady Margaret Road....Tel.267 2936
Antiquarian books.

J. LAVIAN
53-79 Highgate Road....Tel.485 7955
Oriental carpets, rugs, kelims.

M. & M. ORIENTAL GALLERY LTD.
53-79 Highgate Road....Tel.267 5973
Oriental carpets, rugs, tapestries.

N.W.6. West Hampstead

STANLEY BEAL LTD.
41 Fairfax Road....................Tel.328 7525
Silver, Sheffield plate.

TEMPLE BROOKS
12 Mill Lane....................Tel.452 9696
Clocks.

JOHN DENHAM GALLERY
50 Mill Lane....................Tel.794 2635
17th-20th C paintings.

THE DIDDY BOX
82 Mill Lane....................Tel.794 4434
General antiques.

END OF DAY
51 Mill Lane....................Tel.435 8091
Lighting.

G. & F. GILLINGHAM LTD.
4 Crediton Hill....................Tel.435 5644
Furniture, clocks, barometers. Trade only.

PUTNAMS KITCHEN ANTIQUES
72 Mill Lane....................Tel.431 2935
Kitchenware, furniture, china, linen.

SCOPE ANTIQUES
64-66 Willesden Lane....................Tel.328 5833
General antiques.

THE TRINKET BOX
1 Goldhurst Terrace....................Tel.624 4264
Jewelry, silver, china.

N.W.7. Edgware

THE BANK HOUSE GALLERY
8-10 The Broadway, Mill Hill....................Tel.906 3124
Eng. & Continental 19th C oil paintings....................Telex.9229922

GERALD CLARK ANTIQUES LTD.
1 High Street, Mill Hill Village....................Tel.906 0342
Pottery, porcelain, small furniture.

N.W.8. Marylebone, St. John's Wood

ALFIES ANTIQUE MARKET
13-25 Church Street....................see page 26

ANDREAS ANTIQUES
12 Church Street....................Tel.262 1370
General antiques.

BIZARRE
24 Church Street....................Tel.724 1305
Art Deco furniture, pottery, decorative art.

N.W.8.

CHURCH ST. ANTIQUES
8 Church Street........Tel.723 7415
General antiques.

FURNITURE FAIR
22 Church Street........Tel.262 1338
Victorian chairs.

GALLERY OF ANTIQUE COSTUME & TEXTILES
2 Church Street........Tel.723 9981
Costumes, textiles, needlework.

ROD HANRECK ANTIQUES
11 Church Street........Tel.724 9270
General antiques.

JUST DESKS
20 Church Street........Tel.723 7976
Desks, bureaux, filing cabinets.

MAGUS ANTIQUES
4 Church Street........Tel.724 1278
Oriental & European decorative items.

NUMBER 6 ANTIQUES
6 Church Street........Tel.724 2405
General antiques.

S. & H. ANTIQUES
7 Church Street........Tel.724 7118
Porcelain, decorative items.

WELLINGTON GALLERY
1 St. John's Wood High Street........Tel.586 2620
Paintings, watercolors.

N.W.10. Kensal Rise

BROCANTIQUES
31 Linden Avenue........by appointment........Tel.969 7151
Furniture.

For advertising rates and free listing information please contact:

PAIGE PUBLICATIONS
P.O. Box 1384
Rancho Mirage, California 92270
Tel: 619 321 0174 or 619 328 7898

TRADE JOURNALS

ANTIQUE
Publisher: Rodalink, 3rd Floor, 48 Margaret Street, London W1N 7FD. Tel: 01 631 0282
Subscription rates: US$10 1 year (2 issues) US$28 2 years (6 issues)
The amusing international magazine for the trade.

THE ANTIQUE COLLECTOR
Publisher: National Magazine House, 72 Broadwick Street, London W1V 2BP. Tel: 01 439 7144
Subscription rates: US$48 1 year (12 issues) Visa/Mastercard/American Express.
Monthly color magazine. Features interesting articles, trade news, fairs information.
Available at most newsagents in London.

THE ANTIQUE DEALER AND COLLECTORS GUIDE
Publisher: IPC Magazines Ltd., Kings Reach Tower, Stamford Street, London SE1 9LS.
Tel: 01 829 7634
Monthly color magazine. Features news and topical articles, auction news, fairs information.
Available at most newsagents in London.

ANTIQUE FURNITURE & ART WEEKLY BULLETIN
Publisher: H.P. Publishing, 226 Court Oak Road, Harborne, Birmingham B32 2EG.
Tel: 021 426 3300
Subscription rates: US$60 1 year (52 issues) Visa/Mastercard/American Express.
Weekly, newspaper format. Auction calendar, fairs calendar, art prices index, saleroom reports.

ANTIQUES TRADE GAZETTE
Publisher: Metropress Ltd., 17 Whitcomb Street, London WC2H 7PL. Tel: 01 930 4957
Subscription rates: US$75 1 year (50 issues) Visa/Mastercard/American Express.
Weekly, newspaper format. Auction calendar, auction ads & reports, shows, markets. Free specimen copy on request. Also on sale at newspaper kiosk near Sotheby's, Bond Street.

APOLLO
Publisher: Apollo Magazine Ltd., 22 Davies Street, London W1Y 1LH. Tel: 01 629 3061
Subscription rates: US$98 1 year (12 issues)
International art and antiques magazine. All periods covered.

CLOCKS
Publisher: Argus Specialist Publications Ltd., Wolsey House, Wolsey Road, Hemel Hempstead, Herts HP2 4SS. Tel: 0442 41221
Subscription rates: US$47 (accelerated surface post)
Monthly color magazine featuring antique clocks, watches and their makers. Available at some newsagents in London.

THE INTERNATIONAL MAGAZINE FOR THE COLLECTOR OF WATERCOLOURS AND DRAWINGS
Publisher: Consumer Communications Ltd. London House, 271/273 King Street, Hammersmith, London W6 9LZ. Tel: 01 741 8011
Subscription rates: US$12 1 year (4 issues)
Specialist magazine for collectors of watercolors and drawings.

PRINT QUARTERLY
Publisher: Print Quarterly Ltd., 80 Carlton Hill, London NW8 0ER. Tel: 01 625 6332
Subscription rates: US$40 (airmail)
A journal featuring articles on fine prints from the 15th Century to the present.

We are a third generation family run business,
specializing in antique and reproduction
silver, silver plate and antique Sheffield.
Trade welcome.
Unique money back anytime guarantee.

LAPADA
Registered Member
LONDON AND PROVINCIAL ANTIQUE DEALERS ASSOCIATION

Marks Antiques Ltd.

Associated Company: The Curzon Street Silverware Co.
49 Curzon Street, London W.1
Telephone: 01-499 1788

ENGLISH SILVER

A Brief History of Hallmarking And An Appreciation of the Silversmith's Art

By Clive P. Blunt

It is important to understand the part played by silver in the Middle Ages in order to appreciate the esteem in which it is still held. In the fourteenth to the sixteenth centuries, conventional financial institutions did not exist. Much trade was done by barter, and there was little possibility for the successful yeoman farmer or trader to build up his assets beyond the purchase of more land. The coin of the realm was made of sterling silver but without milled edges, and was always susceptible to being "clipped" or debased by the addition of excess alloying materials, and would therefore in either case be reduced in value. It was in this climate that successful businessmen in London set up a Hall to monitor the quality of wrought silver to allow the successful man to turn his success into tangible, convertible wealth. Thus in good times a man's table and house could be full of silver objects from the purely decorative to plates, mugs and cooking utensils. A whole fascinating series of status symbols arose from which a man's wealth could be gauged. For example, the number and size of the salt cellars on the banqueting table, the position of each guest by reference to the standing or master salt gave a very good indication of a man's comparative success.

Pair of Paul Storr entree dishes and soup tureen en suite. London, 1838. Photo courtesy English Heritage, Melrose Place.

Silver design has mirrored not only the development of decorative techniques, the artist's joy in working in precious metals and the relationship between representational images and decoration, but the owner's desire for the display of wealth, sometimes ostentatious, sometimes refined, and his curiosity at the possibilities of the art form.

Since 1300, English silver has by law borne marks which allow us to tell some or all of the following information:

1. The quality of silver—Sterling or Britannia Standard.
2. The maker.
3. The date of manufacture.
4. The application of the duty mark to indicate the payment of Government taxes.

THE STERLING MARK

With the exception of the period 1697 to 1720 when the "Britannia Standard" for silver was 95.8 percent fine, all English silver since 1300 has been of the "sterling" quality. In that year, Edward the First introduced a statute that "no goldsmith should make any wares of gold worse than the 'Touch of Paris' (19 1½5 carats fine) or of silver except for the 'Esterling allay'." Thus the continental standard for silver fixed at 92.5 percent purity with alloys (usually copper) to improve workability, became the English "sterling" standard.

The Britannia Standard of 95.8 percent fine was introduced in 1697 to differentiate it from the silver coin of the same period. The new alloy was softer and did not wear as well as the sterling standard, and was disliked by most silversmiths. The silver of this period was marked with "the figure of a lion's head erased, and the figure of a woman,commonly called Britannia." In June 1720 the Britannia Standard was made optional, and the majority of silversmiths reverted to the sterling standard.

The word "Sterling" actually derives from the earlier reign of King John. Because English coin of the realm in about 1230 contained considerably less silver than earlier made coinage, King John brought silversmiths from Germany and France to increase the silver to a standard of fineness. Not unnaturally the resident English goldsmiths resented this intrusion, and referred to the newcomers rather sneeringly as "Easterlings"—those who have come from the East. Over the passage of time, the "Easterlings" became "Esterlings," and ultimately the word "Sterling" became synonomous with the 92.5 percent silver standard of the silversmiths and with anything or any person of true and tested worth.

Since the year 1300 a mark denoting the sterling quality of silver has been required on every article of silver. Thus, hallmarking was started to ensure that the "ster-

Six bottle cruet by Paul Storr, London 1811. Photo courtesy English Heritage, Melrose Place.

ling" standard of silver was maintained. Penalties for non-performance were severe throughout the ages. The records which are kept at Goldsmith's Hall, London, are fascinating in their records of fines imposed at regular meetings, of varying degrees of severity for non-conformance with the standards; fines escalated with the degree and frequency of the offense. If that were not sufficient, flagrant imposters suffered more; it is recorded in May 1597 that John Moore and Robert Thomas "did, about three months past, make divers parcels of counterfeit plate debased and worse than her Majesty's Standard." Their sentence was to be placed in the pillory with their ears nailed to it, and with a paper over their heads to indicate their crime. The sentence was carried out, and for good measure, one ear of each man was amputated and a fine imposed!

The stamp to designate the sterling silver standard in 1300 was called "the King's Mark," indicated by *Une test de leopart.* The word *Leopart* in heraldic French means a lion passant, taken from the arms of the sovereign, that was stamped on English silver to demonstrate the "sterling quality."

The full lion passant was adopted by the Goldsmith's Hall in London in 1544, to counteract the nefarious actions of Henry VIII in debasing the silver coinage to boost his coffers. It is indicated that whatever the King may do at the mint, purchasers of plate with the lion passant could assure that it was still of the "sterling" standard. The new mark of the full lion passant was used in addition to the lion's head on London silver, but as other assay offices were founded in major towns in England, the full lion passant was adopted instead of (although initially as well as) the lion's head to denote the sterling quality. However, the lion's head (and later the leopard's head) was used as the heraldic device of the London assay office, and still remains in use today.

Frontal face of the Lion Passant Guardant dating from 1300

Lion Passant Adopted 1544

MAKER'S MARK

In 1363 it was ordained that all Master Goldsmiths should have a mark of their own. Sometimes the initial letter of their names, sometimes a symbol denoting their name (e.g. Andrew Raven used a bird). Upon the adoption of the Britannia Standard in April 1697 a complete new set of marks were used until June 1720 involving the use of the first two letters of their last name, thus—

Lawrence Coles, April 1697

When in 1720 the standard optionally reverted to 92.5 percent fine the practice of using the initial letters of the first and last names was revived. Two famous marks which indicate this are—

Hester Bateman June 1776

Paul Storr February 18, 1808

Although the Britannia Standard had not proved popular with most silversmiths, owing to the difficulty of satisfactorily working the higher quality, some silversmiths continued sing it. Paul de Lamerie, the revered Huguenot silversmith, did not enter a sterling mark until 1732, over twelve years after the change.

TOWN MARKS

Until 1423 the right to assay silver was the jealously guarded prerogative of London. Silver was made provincially before that time but was in that case unmarked or bore the device or mark of the silversmith at his own discretion. In 1423 seven provincial offices were opened.

Birmingham

Lincoln

Newcastle

Some of these assay offices functioned for only a short while, and then were closed and provincial silver from some of these offices carries a substantial premium over the more common London marks.

Henry VI licensed seven provincial cities to be allowed to mark their own silver, and the development of recognized guilds outside the Captial City of London became sanctioned. The cities so licensed were Newcastle, York, Lincoln, Norwich, Bristol, Salisbury, and Coventry.

Fine pair of Paul Storr cast candlesticks, London 1816, together with chamberstick of unusual shape, London 1831, also by Storr. Photo courtesy English Heritage, Melrose Place.

In 1773 the Cities of Sheffield and Birmingham were also sanctioned to hallmark silver, and an amusing story is told of how a number of worthies from these two cities, amongst them Matthew Boulton, one of the greatest entrepreneurs, engineers, designers and silversmiths of the late eighteenth and early nineteenth centuries, repaired to a tavern called "The Crown and Anchor" after having been told of the decision to grant them hallmarking rights. After a period of convivial celebration, the discussion of the emblems to be adopted arose, and after a period of impasse it was suggested that a coin be tossed and the way it fell determine the device for the city concerned, one the Crown and the other the Anchor, taken from the name of the hostelry in which they were celebrating. If this story is true, it may serve to explain why Birmingham, a city as far from the sea as any in England, bears the nautical anchor as its town assay mark.

Oval, two handled, footed tray by Paul Storr bearing full Royal Coat of Arms and motto of King George III, surmounted by a second coat of arms and civil motto of the Order of the Bath. Assayed London 1814. Photo courtesy of English Heritage, Melrose Place.

DATE

1681

The adoption of the date letter to denote the year of manufacture is ascribed to the year 1478. Since that time the letters of the alphabet (A to U or V, omitting J) have been used in twenty year cycles. No silver has been found with the date letter for 1478; the first piece recorded has the letter B for 1479. The date of a piece can be accurately established since in each cycle there have been minor

1719

1739

changes in the shape of the cartouche (shield) enclosing the letter, and the letter itself has gone through a number of changes from upper to lower case, from Gothic to Greek and so on.

1799

1879

THE DUTY MARKS

Duty for all plate hallmarked was levied from 1719 at a rate of sixpence per ounce (considerable sum by modern standards), and although licensing of goldsmiths was substituted thirty-eight years later, the Crown continued to levy tax on goldsmiths in some form up to 1890. During the period 1784 to 1890 the Sovereign's head was used in conjunction with the other hallmarks to indicate that duty has been paid. The duty mark has been struck every year since 1786 using a punch for the same form as the other hallmarks. For the first year and a half, however, the mark was stuck 'in intaglio,' that is etched into the silver rather than raised out of it in relief.

George II inkstand by Paul de Lamerie; London 1739.

Clive Blunt is the President of English Heritage
8424 Melrose Place, Los Angeles, California 90069
Telephone: (213) 655-5946

SILVER HALLMARKS

London

1678	a
1679	b
1680	c
1681	d
1682	e
1683	f
1684	g
1685	h
1686	i
1687	k
1688	l
1689	m
1690	n
1691	o
1692	p
1693	q
1694	r
1695	s
1696	t
1697	a b
1698	c
1699	d
1700	e
1701	f
1702	g
1703	h
1704	i
1705	k
1706	l
1707	m
1708	n
1709	o
1710	p
1711	q
1712	r
1713	s
1714	t
1715	v
1716	A
1717	B
1718	C
1719	D
1720	E
1721	F
1722	G
1723	H
1724	I
1725	K
1726	L
1727	M
1728	N
1729	O
1730	P
1731	Q
1732	R
1733	S
1734	T
1735	V
1736	a
1737	b
1738	c
1739	d
1739	d
1740	e
1741	f
1742	g
1743	h
1744	i
1745	k
1746	l
1747	m
1748	n
1749	o
1750	p
1751	q
1752	r
1753	s
1754	t
1755	u
1756	A
1757	B
1758	C
1759	D
1760	E
1761	F
1762	G
1763	H
1764	I
1765	K
1766	L
1767	M
1768	N
1769	O
1770	P
1771	Q
1772	R
1773	S
1774	T
1775	U
1776	a
1777	b
1778	c
1779	d
1780	e
1781	f
1782	g
1783	h
1784	i
1785	k
1786	l
1787	m
1788	n
1789	o
1790	p
1791	q
1792	r
1793	s
1794	t
1795	u
1796	A
1797	B
1798	C
1799	D
1800	E
1801	F
1802	G
1803	H
1804	I
1805	K
1806	L
1807	M
1808	N
1809	O
1810	P
1811	Q
1812	R
1813	S
1814	T
1815	U
1816	a
1817	b
1818	c
1819	d
1820	e
1821	f
1822	g
1823	h
1824	i
1825	k
1826	l
1827	m
1828	n
1829	o
1830	p
1831	q
1832	r
1833	s
1834	t
1835	u
1836	A
1837	B
1838	C
1839	D
1840	E
1841	F
1842	G
1843	H
1844	I
1845	K
1846	L
1847	M
1848	N
1849	O
1850	P
1851	Q
1852	R
1853	S
1854	T
1855	U
1856	a
1857	b
1858	c
1859	d
1860	e
1861	f
1862	g
1863	h
1864	i
1865	k
1866	l
1867	m
1868	n
1869	o
1870	p
1871	q
1872	r
1873	s
1874	t
1875	u
1876	A
1877	B
1878	C
1879	D
1880	E
1881	F
1882	G
1883	H
1884	I
1885	K
1886	L
1887	M
1888	N
1889	O
1890	P
1891	Q
1892	R
1893	S
1894	T
1895	U
1896	a
1897	b
1898	c
1899	d
1900	e
1901	f
1902	g
1903	h
1904	i
1905	k
1906	l
1907	m
1908	n
1909	o
1910	p
1911	q
1912	r
1913	s
1914	t
1915	u
1916	a
1917	b
1918	c
1919	d
1920	e
1921	f
1922	g
1923	h
1924	i
1925	k
1926	l
1927	m
1928	n
1929	o
1930	p
1931	q
1932	r
1933	s
1934	t
1935	u
1936	A
1937	B
1938	C
1939	D
1940	E
1941	F
1942	G
1943	H
1944	I
1945	K
1946	L
1947	M
1948	N
1949	O
1950	P
1951	Q
1952	R
1953	S
1954	T
1955	U
1956	a
1957	b
1958	c
1959	d
1960	e
1961	f
1962	g
1963	h
1964	i
1965	k
1966	l
1967	m
1968	n
1969	o
1970	p
1971	q
1972	r
1973	s
1974	t
1975	A
1976	B
1977	C
1978	D
1979	E
1980	F
1981	G
1982	H
1983	I
1984	K
1985	L

Birmingham

1773	A
1774	B
1775	C
1776	D
1777	E
1778	F
1779	G
1780	H
1781	I
1782	K
1783	L

1784	M
1785	N

1786	O
1787	P
1788	Q
1789	R
1790	S
1791	T
1792	U
1793	V
1794	W
1795	X
1796	Y
1797	Z
1798	a
1799	b
1800	c
1801	d
1802	e
1803	f
1804	g
1805	h
1806	i
1807	j
1808	k
1809	l
1810	m
1811	n
1812	o
1813	p
1814	q
1815	r
1816	s
1817	t
1818	u
1819	v
1820	w
1821	x
1822	y
1823	z
1824	A
1825	B
1826	C
1827	D
1828	E
1829	F
1830	G
1831	H
1832	I
1833	K

1834	L
1835	M
1836	N
1837	O

1838	P
1839	Q
1840	R
1841	S
1842	T
1843	U
1844	V
1845	W
1846	X
1847	Y
1848	Z

1849	A
1850	B
1851	C
1852	D
1853	E
1854	F
1855	G
1856	H
1857	I
1858	J
1859	K
1860	L
1861	M
1862	N
1863	O
1864	P
1865	Q
1866	R
1867	S
1868	T
1869	U
1870	V
1871	W
1872	X
1873	Y
1874	Z

1875	a
1876	b
1877	c
1878	d
1879	e
1880	f
1881	g
1882	h
1883	i
1884	k
1885	l
1886	m
1887	n
1888	o
1889	p
1890	q

1891	r
1892	s
1893	t
1894	u
1895	v
1896	w
1897	x
1898	y
1899	z

1900	a
1901	b
1902	c
1903	d
1904	e
1905	f
1906	g
1907	h
1908	i
1909	k
1910	l
1911	m
1912	n
1913	o
1914	p
1915	q
1916	r
1917	s
1918	t
1919	u
1920	v
1921	w
1922	x
1923	y
1924	z
1925	A
1926	B
1927	C
1928	D
1929	E
1930	F
1931	G
1932	H
1933	J
1934	K
1935	L
1936	M
1937	N
1938	O
1939	P
1940	Q
1941	R
1942	S
1943	T
1944	U
1945	V
1946	W
1947	X
1948	Y
1949	Z

1950	A
1951	B
1952	C
1953	D
1954	E
1955	F
1956	G
1957	H
1958	J
1959	K
1960	L
1961	M
1962	N
1963	O
1964	P
1965	Q
1966	R
1967	S
1968	T
1969	U
1970	V
1971	W
1972	X

1973	Y

1974	Z

1975	A
1976	B
1977	C
1978	D
1979	E
1980	F
1981	G
1982	H
1983	J
1984	K
1985	L

Sheffield

1773	E
1774	F
1775	N
1776	R
1777	h
1778	S
1779	A
1780	T
1781	D
1782	G
1783	B
1784	I
1785	Y
1786	k
1787	T
1788	w
1789	M
1790	L
1791	P
1792	u
1793	n
1794	m
1795	q
1796	Z
1797	X
1798	V
1799	E
1800	N
1801	H
1802	M
1803	F
1804	G
1805	B
1806	A
1807	S
1808	P
1809	K
1810	L
1811	C
1812	D
1813	R
1814	W
1815	O
1816	T
1817	X
1818	I
1819	V
1820	Q
1821	Y
1822	Z
1823	U
1824	a
1825	b
1826	c
1827	d
1828	e
1829	f
1830	g
1831	h
1832	k
1833	l
1834	m
1835	p
1836	q
1837	r
1838	s
1839	t
1840	u
1841	V
1842	X
1843	Z
1844	A
1845	B
1846	C
1847	D
1848	E
1849	F
1850	G
1851	H
1852	I
1853	K
1854	L
1855	M
1856	N
1857	O
1858	P
1859	R
1860	S
1861	T
1862	U
1863	V
1864	W
1865	X
1866	Y
1867	Z
1868	A
1869	B
1870	C
1871	D
1872	E
1873	F
1874	G
1875	H
1876	J
1877	K
1878	L
1879	M
1880	N
1881	O
1882	P
1883	Q
1884	R
1885	S
1886	T
1887	U
1888	V
1889	W
1890	X
1891	Y
1892	Z
1893	a
1894	b
1895	c
1896	d
1897	e
1898	f
1899	g
1900	h
1901	i
1902	k
1903	l
1904	m
1905	n
1906	o
1907	p
1908	q
1909	r
1910	s
1911	t
1912	u
1913	v
1914	w
1915	x
1916	y
1917	z
1918	a
1919	b
1920	c
1921	d
1922	e
1923	f
1924	g
1925	h
1926	i
1927	k
1928	l
1929	m
1930	n
1931	o
1932	p
1933	q
1934	r
1935	s
1936	t
1937	u
1938	v
1939	w
1940	x
1941	y
1942	z
1943	A
1944	B
1945	C
1946	D
1947	E
1948	F
1949	G
1950	H
1951	I
1952	K
1953	L
1954	M
1955	N
1956	O
1957	P
1958	Q
1959	R
1960	S
1961	T
1962	U
1963	V
1964	W
1965	X
1966	Y
1967	Z
1968	A
1969	B
1970	C
1971	D
1972	E
1973	F
1974	G
1975	A
1976	B
1977	C
1978	D
1979	E
1980	F
1981	G
1982	H
1983	J
1984	K
1985	L

Edinburgh

1705	A
1706	B
1707	C
1708	D
1709	E
1710	F
1711	G
1712	H
1713	I
1714	K
1715	L
1716	M
1717	N
1718	O
1719	P
1720	Q
1721	R
1722	S
1723	T
1724	U
1725	V
1726	W
1727	X
1728	Y
1729	Z
1730	A
1731	B
1732	C
1733	D
1734	E
1735	F
1736	G
1737	H
1738	I
1739	K
1740	L
1741	M
1742	N
1743	O
1744	P
1745	Q
1746	R
1747	S
1748	T
1749	U
1750	V
1751	W
1752	X
1753	Y
1754	Z
1755	A
1756	B
1757	C
1758	D
1759	E
1760	F
1761	G
1762	H
1763	I
1764	K
1765	L
1766	M
1767	N
1768	O
1769	P
1770	Q
1771	R
1772	S
1773	T
1774	U
1775	V
1776	X
1777	Y
1778	Z
1779	Y
1780	A
1781	B
1782	C
1783	D
1784	E
1785	F
1786	G
1787	G
1788	H
1789	I J
1790	K
1791	L
1792	M
1793	N
1794	O
1795	P
1796	Q
1797	R
1798	S
1799	T
1800	U
1801	V
1802	W
1803	X
1804	Y
1805	Z
1806	a
1807	b
1808	c
1809	d
1810	e
1811	f
1812	g
1813	h
1814	i
1815	j
1816	k
1817	l
1818	m
1819	n
1820	o
1821	p
1822	q
1823	r
1824	s
1825	t
1826	u
1827	v
1828	w
1829	x
1830	y
1831	z
1832	A
1833	B
1834	C
1835	D
1836	E
1837	F
1838	G
1839	H
1840	I
1841	K
1842	L
1843	M
1844	N
1845	O
1846	P
1847	Q
1848	R
1849	S
1850	T
1851	U
1852	V
1853	W
1854	X
1855	Y
1856	Z
1857	A
1858	B
1859	C
1860	D
1861	E
1862	F
1863	G
1864	H
1865	I
1866	K
1867	L
1868	M
1869	N
1870	O
1871	P
1872	Q
1873	R
1874	S
1875	T
1876	U
1877	V
1878	W
1879	X
1880	Y
1881	Z
1882	a
1883	b
1884	c
1885	d
1886	e
1887	f
1888	g
1889	h
1890	i
1891	k
1892	l
1893	m
1894	n
1895	o
1896	p
1897	q
1898	r
1899	s
1900	t
1901	u
1902	w
1903	x
1904	y
1905	z
1906	A
1907	B
1908	C
1909	D
1910	E
1911	F
1912	G
1913	H
1914	I
1915	K
1916	L
1917	M
1918	N
1919	O
1920	P
1921	Q
1922	R
1923	S
1924	T
1925	U
1926	V
1927	W
1928	X
1929	Y
1930	Z
1931	A
1932	B
1933	C
1934	D
1935	E
1936	F
1937	G
1938	H
1939	I
1940	K
1941	L
1942	M
1943	N
1944	O
1945	P
1946	Q
1947	R
1948	S
1949	T
1950	U
1951	V
1952	W
1953	X
1954	Y
1955	Z
1956	A
1957	B
1958	C
1959	D
1960	E
1961	F
1962	G
1963	H
1964	I
1965	K
1966	L
1967	M
1968	N
1969	O
1970	P
1971	Q
1972	R
1973-4	S
1975	A
1976	B
1977	C
1978	D
1979	E
1980	F
1981	G
1982	H
1983	I
1984	K
1985	L

35,000 square feet of warehousing.

We carry a large, varied stock of:

Walnut, mahogany, oak and pine furniture running through from Georgian, Victorian, Edwardian, plus some earlier pieces; also 1920's shipping goods.

There is also a large stock of smalls and collectables i.e. china, porcelain, glass and decorative items.

We aim to carry stock to suit all markets - why not pay us a visit for your next requirements?

CONTAINER PACKING CARRIED OUT AT VERY COMPETITIVE PRICES

We offer facilities for packing 20ft and 40ft containers by expert packers. All documentation attended to.

We are within easy reach of London by rail and road.

Also within easy reach of east coast shipping ports and ferry terminals.

F.G. BRUSCHWEILER (Antiques) LTD.

41-67 Lower Lambricks, Rayleigh, Essex SS6 7EN
Telephone: Rayleigh (0268) 773761
(0268) 773932
After hours: Maldon (0621) 828152

OUT OF TOWN

Essex

F.G. BRUSCHWEILER (ANTIQUES) LTD.
41-67 Lower Lambricks, RAYLEIGH Tel.0268 773761
18th-19th C furniture, shipping goods.

HATCH PINE ANTIQUES
Hatch Farm, Ongar Road, BRENTWOOD Tel.0277 72202
Antique & repro. pine.

KELVEDON ANTIQUES
90 High Street, KELVEDON Tel.0376 70557
18th-early 19th C furniture.

MILLERS ANTIQUES KELVEDON
46 High Street, KELVEDON Tel.0376 70098
17th-19th C furniture Telex.987562

G.T. RATCLIFFE LTD.
Durwards Hall, KELVEDON Tel.0376 70234
18th-19th C furniture. Trade only.

RUNDELLS ANTIQUES
London Road, HARLOW Tel.0279 22906
17th-19th C furniture, porcelain, paintings, rugs, prints.

STONE HALL ANTIQUES
Down Hall Road, MATCHING GREEN, nr. Harlow Tel.0279 731440
17th-19th C furniture.

Kent

CHEVERTONS OF EDENBRIDGE LTD.
Taylour House, High Street, EDENBRIDGE Tel.0732 863196
17th-19th C furniture.

DEREK ROBERTS ANTIQUES
24 Shipbourne Road, TONBRIDGE Tel.0732 358986
Clocks. Illustrated catalogue £5.

SUTTON VALENCE ANTIQUES
SUTTON VALENCE, nr. Maidstone Tel.0622 843333
18th-19th C furniture, porcelain, metalware, silver.

TUDOR COTTAGE ANTIQUES
22-23 Shipbourne Road, TONBRIDGE Tel.0732 351719
Furniture, silver, porcelain, brass, copper.

Middlesex

THE ANTIQUES WAREHOUSE
34 Rockingham Road, UXBRIDGE Tel.0895 56963
General antiques, shipping goods.

JOHN IVES BOOKSELLER
5 Normanhurst Dr., St. Margarets, TWICKENHAM Tel.01 892 6265
Books on antiques, costume, needlework, architecture. By appointment.

PHELPS LTD.
133-135 St. Margarets Rd., St. Margarets. TWICKENHAM Tel.01 892 1778
Victorian & Edwardian furniture.

Surrey

ANTIQUE MART
72-74 Hill Rise, RICHMOND Tel.01 940 6942
18th-19th C furniture.

APOLLO GALLERIES
61/65/67 South End, CROYDON Tel.01 681 3727
Paintings, bronzes, porcelain, furniture, objets d'art.

KEITH ATKINSON
59 Brighton Road, SOUTH CROYDON Tel.01 688 5559
Furniture, shipping goods.

CHURCH HOUSE ANTIQUES
42 Church Street, WEYBRIDGE Tel.0932 42190
18th-19th C furniture, silver, jewelry, clocks, china.

THE CLOCK SHOP
64 Church Street, WEYBRIDGE Tel.0932 40407
Clocks. Restoration.

MOLLIE EVANS
84 Hill Rise, RICHMOND Tel.01 948 0182
Country furniture, pottery, samplers.

G.E. GRIFFIN
43a Brighton Road, SOUTH CROYDON Tel.01 688 3130
General antiques.

J. HARTLEY ANTIQUES LTD.
186 High Street, RIPLEY Tel.0483 224318
18th-19th C furniture, paintings.

HILL RISE ANTIQUES
26 Hill Rise, RICHMOND Tel.01 948 1140
18th-19th C furniture, silver.

PAUL KEEN ANTIQUES
195-197 Brighton Road, CROYDON Tel.01 688 1316
18th-19th C furniture, paintings.

RIPLEY ANTIQUES
67 High Street, RIPLEY Tel.0483 224981
18th-19th C furniture, decorative items.

R. SAUNDERS
71 Queen's Road, WEYBRIDGE Tel.0932 42601
17th-19th C furniture, barometers, silver, porcelain.

ANTHONY WELLING ANTIQUES
Broadway Barn, High Street, RIPLEY Tel.0483 225384
17th-18th C country furniture, metalware.

WEYBRIDGE ANTIQUES
66-68 Church Street, WEYBRIDGE Tel.0932 52503
17th-19th C furniture, paintings, silver, jewelry, porcelain.

Sussex

THE ANTIQUE CENTRE
Angel Street, PETWORTH Tel.0798 43221
Furniture, paintings, porcelain, silver.

ANTIQUE WORKSHOP (prop. Mike Barratt)
22 Marine Place, WORTHING Tel.0903 209395
Pine & oak furniture, shipping goods.

BRITISH ANTIQUE EXPORTERS
School Close, Queen Elizabeth Ave., BURGESS HILL Tel.04446 45577
Large stock of general antiques.

JOHN G. MORRIS LTD.
Market Square, PETWORTH Tel.0798 42305
17th-19th C furniture, clocks, bronzes.

MICHAEL J. O'NEILL
Swan House, Market Square, PETWORTH Tel.0798 42616
17th-18th C English furniture, clocks.

PINE FURNITURE (prop. Mary Sautter)
6 Station Street, LEWES Tel.0273 474842
Pine furniture.

E. STREETER & DAUGHTER
Clock House, Lombard Street, PETWORTH Tel.0798 42239
Jewelry, silver.

Bath

The historical city of Bath is located 110 miles west of London. The journey by comfortable high-speed train takes 1¼ hours and trains depart from Paddington Station, Praed Street, W.2. (info. tel. 262 6767). By car — take the M4 to Junction 18 then the A46 — it takes approximately 2 hours.

Bath owes its origin to the mineral waters which were discovered in Roman times, but this gracious city became the most fashionable resort during the Georgian period when the genius of architects like John Wood, John Palmer and Robert Adam designed terraced houses in the shape of crescents and squares giving this city the supreme elegance that still exists today. Bath Abbey is to be found in the heart of the city and across the courtyard are the Roman Baths and Pump Room. A guided tour of the Baths provides a fascinating insight into the history of the City.

Two miles out of town is Claverton Manor — this large Georgian manor, set in a splendid 55 acre estate, houses the American Museum in Britain. The eighteen period-furnished rooms recreate interiors of early American homes with a fine collection of 17th-19th century American furnishings and paintings. (Open Tuesday-Sunday 2pm-5pm).

Following are some of the antiques dealers in the city, but not to be overlooked are the dealers in nearby Bradford on Avon. For further details contact The Secretary, Bath & Bradford on Avon Antique Dealers Association, Trim Bridge, 1 Queen Street, Bath, Avon BA1 1HE. Tel: 0225 316957.

BATH DEALERS

BRYERS ANTIQUES
12a Manvers Street Tel.60535
Silver, glass ceramics, furniture.

ROBIN & JAN COLEMAN ANTIQUES
27b Belvedere, Lansdown Tel.316216
Decorative items.

COLLETON HOUSE GALLERY LTD.
8a Quiet Street Tel.28806
Paintings, bronzes, French furniture.

JOHN CROFT ANTIQUES
3 George Street Tel.66211
Fine furniture, paintings, clocks.

ANDREW DANDO
4 Wood St., Queen Square Tel.22702
Porcelain, pottery, furniture.

GERALD DEACON
2 Wood St., Queen Square Tel.25907
Fine furniture, porcelain.

D. & B. DICKINSON
22 New Bond Street Tel.66502
Silver, jewlery.

BRIAN & ANGELA DOWNES ANTIQUES
9 Broad Street Tel.65352
Fine furniture, porcelain.

GENE & SALLY FOSTER ANTIQUES
27A Belvedere, Lansdown Tel.28256
Country furniture, folk art.

SIMON & CLAIRE FREEMAN ANTIQUES
27b Belvedere, Lansdown Tel.316216
Unusual decorative items.

M.A. & D.A. HUGHES
11 Pulteney Bridge Tel.65782
Silver, jewelry.

JADIS LTD.
The Old Bank, 17 Walcot Bldgs., London Road Tel.338797
Country furniture, decorative items.

JOHN KEIL LTD.
10 Quiet Street Tel.63176
17th-19th C furniture, metalware.

LANSDOWN ANTIQUES
23 Belvedere, Lansdown Tel.313417
17th-19th C furniture, metalware, decorative items.

LANTERN GALLERY
9 George Street Tel.63727
Decorative, botanical & natural history prints.

MacHUMBLE ANTIQUES
11 Queen Street Tel.62751
17th-19th C furniture, metalware, samplers, objets d'art.

E.P. MALLORY & SON LTD.
5 Old Bond Street . . . Tel.65885
1-4 Bridge Street
Silver, Sheffield plate, clocks, jewelry.

No. TWELVE QUEEN STREET
12 Queen Street . . . Tel.62363
17th-19th C country furniture, decorative items.

RICHARD PARKER LTD.
Trim Bridge, 1 Queen Street . . . Tel.330257
17th-19th C furniture, decorative items.

PICCADILLY ANTIQUES
1-2 Piccadilly, London Road . . . Tel.332779
Folk art, country furniture.

QUEEN'S PARADE ANTIQUES
35 Gay Street . . . Tel.20337
18th-19th C furniture, decorative items.

QUIET STREET ANTIQUES
3 Quiet Street . . . Tel.315727
18th-19th C furniture, clocks, bronzes.

T.E. ROBINSON ANTIQUES
3&4 Bartlett Street . . . Tel.63982
Fine furniture, glassware, decorative items.

SHEILA SMITH ANTIQUES
10 a Queen Street . . . Tel.60568
Fans, needlework, glass, treen.

ANTIQUES MARKETS AND CENTERS

Bath Antique Market
Guinea Lane, Lansdown Road
90 dealers
Open Wednesday 7am-3pm

Bartlett Street Antique Market
7-10 Bartlett Street
Tel: 0225 66689, 50 dealers
Open Monday-Saturday 9.30am-5pm
Wednesday 8am-5pm

Bath Saturday Antique Market
Upper Beaufort Hotel, Walcot Street
Tel: 0225 317837, 50 dealers

Great Western Antique Centre
Bartlett Street
Tel: 0225 24243, 60 dealers
Open Monday-Saturday 9.30am-5pm,
One day market every Wednesday 7.30am-4.30pm featuring 40 dealers on the lower ground floor.

Paragon Antiques Market
3 Bladud Buildings, The Paragon
Tel: 0225 63715
Open Wednesday 6.30am-3.30pm

West of England Antiques Fair
Assembly Rooms, Bennet Street, Bath, Avon.
Tel: 0225 330029
May 12-16
Organizer: Anne Campbell MacInnes, 9 George Street, Bath, Avon.
Tel: 0225 63727

Brighton

The seaside resort of Brighton is 53 miles from London and the journey takes just under 1 hour by train with frequent departures from Victoria Station, Buckingham Palace Road, S.W.1. (info. tel. 928 5100). By car — take the A23 then M23 — it takes approximately 2 hours from Central London.

This lively resort can provide a delightful day trip, particularly if the weather is nice.

Brighton boasts some of the finest Regency architecture in the country, inspired by the Prince Regent, later George IV, who used the Royal Pavilion as his summer palace. This pseudo-Indian style palace was built in 1815, at a time when Oriental decor was very fashionable. It is decorated with pinnacles, minarets, latticed balconies and onion domes. There are 23 state rooms in the palace, mainly decorated in the Chinese style and with many pieces of Regency design from the Royal Collection.

Brighton's Art Gallery and Museum on Church Street was originally designed in 1803 as stables and riding house for the Prince Regent. In 1873, however, the stables were converted into a Museum and Lending Library. There have been many improvements since and the Museum now houses a major Art Deco collection, porcelain, oil paintings, watercolors, musical instruments, furniture and a costume collection covering the period from 1780-1970. (Open Monday-Saturday 10am-5.45pm, Sunday 2pm-5.45pm).

A few minutes walk from the Royal Pavilion, one wanders into The Lanes, a maze of small attractive shops which have been converted from 17th century fishing cottages. Many of these shops sell antiques and, although this is the most concentrated area of antique shops in the area, there is an abundance of dealers in other areas of Brighton and neighboring towns along the coast.

BRIGHTON DEALERS

ADRIAN ALAN LTD.
15c Prince Albert Street Tel.25015
17th-19th C furniture, clocks, bronzes, porcelain.

ANGEL ANTIQUES
16 Church Road Tel.737955
General antiques.

ATTIC ANTIQUES
23 & 32 Ship Street Tel.29464
General antiques.

BRUTON-BRIGHTON
31-32 Meeting House Lane Tel.26591
General antiques.

PETER CARMICHAEL
33 Upper North Street Tel.28072
Barometers, general antiques.

JAMES DOYLE ANTIQUES
9 Union Street Tel.23694
Jewelry, silver.

HALLMARKS
4 Union Street Tel.725477
Silver, jewelry, clocks.

DAVID HAWKINS (BRIGHTON) LTD.
15b Prince Albert Street Tel.21357
General antiques, arms & armour.

THE HOUSE OF ANTIQUES
25 Meeting House Lane Tel.27680
General antiques.

LENNOX ANTIQUES
53 Upper North Street Tel.29409
General antiques.

H. MILLER (ANTIQUES) LTD.
22a Ship Street Tel.26255
Silver, jewelry.

COLIN PAGE ANTIQUARIAN BOOKS
36 Duke Street Tel.25954
16th-20th C antiquarian books.

Brighton Antiques Fair

8-11 July

Penman Antiques Fairs

Corn Exchange, Royal Pavilion Grounds

Tel 04447 2514

75 stands, mostly 1870 datelined
Adm: £1.50 incl Catalogue

TREVOR PHILIP & SONS LTD.
2 Prince Albert Street Tel.202119
Scientific instruments, marine paintings.

RESNERS
1 Meeting House Lane Tel.29127
Jewelry.

S. & L. SIMMONS
9 Meeting House Lane Tel.27949
Jewelry, silver.

SOUTH COAST ANTIQUES LTD.
3 Kensington Place Tel.609828
General antiques.

SUSSEX COMMEMORATIVE WARE CENTRE
88 Western Road, Hove Tel.773911
19th-20th C collectors' items.

TAPSELL ANTIQUES
59 Middle Street Tel.28341
General antiques.

E. & B. WHITE
43-47 Upper North Street Tel.28706
Oak furniture.

DAVID WIGDOR
44 Victoria Street Tel.25908
General antiques.

THE WITCH BALL
48 Meeting House Lane Tel.26618
Prints, maps, caricatures.

YELLOW FROG (BRIGHTON) LTD.
10-11 Meeting House Lane Tel.25497
Jewelry, silver, porcelain.

YELLOW LANTERN ANTIQUES LTD.
34 & 65b Holland Road, Hove Tel.771572
Eng. furniture, clocks, bronzes, porcelain.

19 MIDDLE STREET ANTIQUES
19 Middle Street Tel.727791
Furniture, china, glass.

The discerning business traveller's friend — an elegant, Elizabethan-style hotel set in 100 acres of beautifully-landscaped grounds yet only eight minutes by regular courtesy bus (every 15 mins) from London Gatwick Airport and express train services to London and Brighton. The Copthorne has 223 rooms and facilities include two restaurants, a seven-court squash club, sauna, solarium and gymnasium. There is also a croquet lawn and putting green. Extensive conference facilities are available.

West Sussex, RH10 3PG, England, Tel: (0342) 714971, Telex: 95500 COPTEL-G

Windsor

The Royal Borough of Windsor is 21 miles from Central London. The journey by train takes approximately 25 minutes and departures are from Paddington Station, Praed Street, W.2. (info. tel. 262 6767). By car — take the M4 then A308 — it takes about one hour from Central London.

Windsor has been the home of Royalty since the 12th century and even today Windsor Castle is the largest inhabited castle in the world. The castle precincts are open to the public, and visitors are admitted to the State Apartments when the Queen is not in official residence. A visit to the Queen's Dolls' House should not be missed. It is a fully working model palace given to Queen Mary in 1924. The house was designed by Sir Edwin Lutyens on a scale of 12:1 and involved over 1500 craftsmen.

A pedestrian bridge over the Thames connects Windsor with Eton, famous for its College and impressive chapel, which was founded in 1440 by Henry VI. Eton College is open daily from 2pm-5pm and, within the College, is the Myers Museum of Antiquities which houses a fine Egyptological collection. Eton has a number of interesting shops, with many antiques dealers located in the High Street. There are also some good eating places here — I recommend the Christopher in Eton High Street for lunch and their restaurant upstairs, the Peacock, has a reputation for excellent food served in the Edwardian atmosphere of the turn of the century.

WINDSOR DEALERS

ROGER BARNETT
91 High Street, Eton Tel.867785
General antiques.

GUY BOUSFIELD
58 Thames Street Tel.864575
Georgian furniture.

EATONS OF ETON LTD.
62-63 High Street Tel.860337
17th-19th C furniture, porcelain, silver, clocks.

ETON ANTIQUE BOOK SHOP
88 High Street, Eton Tel.855534
Antiquarian books, prints.

ETON COTTAGE ANTIQUES
60 High Street, Eton Tel.856329
General antiques.

ETON GALLERY
116 High Street, Eton Tel.865147
18th-19th C furniture.

GREENGRASS ANTIQUES
34 Frances Road Tel.865627
General antiques.

GRIFFIN GALLERY
89 Grove Road Tel.853658
Goss china, paintings, prints.

HOY ANTIQUES
17 Kings Road Tel.865555
Furniture, silver, china.

J. MANLEY
27 High Street, Eton Tel.865647
18th-20th C watercolors, prints.

PETER J. MARTIN
40 High Street, Eton Tel.864901
Furniture, metalware, shipping goods.

MOSTLY BOXES
52b High Street Tel.850232
18th-19th C caddies, wooden boxes.

MOSTLY FURNITURE
92 High Street, Eton Tel.858470
Furniture, boxes.

O'CONNOR BROTHERS
59 St. Leonards Road Tel.866732
General antiques.

JOHN A. PEARSON LTD.
127-128 High Street, Eton Tel.860850
18th-19th C Eng. furniture, works of art.

"ROBERTS"
12a Thames Street Tel.866268
Silver.

ULLA STAFFORD
65 High Street, Eton Tel.859625
18th C furniture, porcelain.

STUDIO 101
101 High Street, Eton Tel.863333
18th-19th C furniture, pottery, metalware, prints.

MAURICE TAFFLER LTD.
17 High Street, Eton Tel.864711
General antiques.

TIMES PAST ANTIQUES LTD.
59 High Street, Eton Tel.857018
Clocks, watches, furniture, silver.

TURKS HEAD ANTIQUES
98 High Street, Eton Tel.863939
Silver, jewelry, lace.

VICTORIA ANTIQUES
21 Kings Road Tel.857611
Jewelry, silver, objets d'art.

WINDSOR ANTIQUE GALLERY
45 Thames Street Tel.852965
General antiques.

WINDSOR ANTIQUES
80 High Street, Eton Tel.860752
18th-19th C furniture, longcase clocks.

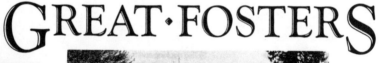

GREAT·FOSTERS

Great Fosters was once a Royal hunting lodge in the heart of Windsor Forest and for nearly four centuries the stately Elizabethan home of many notable families. Great Fosters to-day is no ordinary hotel. It is a very English institution – a place of great charm and tradition – and a scheduled Grade I Historic Monument. For over half a century it has entertained a galaxy of important and discriminating guests from the film star world, from high society and from big business. Great Fosters maintains the atmosphere and splendour of the past and is renowned worldwide as England's *most distinguished* country hotel.

Built 1550 A.D.
At Egham in the
County of Surrey

Tel (0784) 33822
Telex 944441
TW20 9UR

SOVEREIGNS OF ENGLAND

William I	1066-1087
William II	1087-1100
Henry I	1100-1135
Stephen	1135-1154
Henry II	1154-1189
Richard I	1189-1199
John	1199-1216
Henry III	1216-1272
Edward I	1273-1307
Edward II	1307-1327
Edward III	1327-1377
Richard II	1377-1399
Henry IV	1399-1413
Henry V	1413-1422
Henry VI	1422-1461
Edward IV	1461-1483
Edward V	1483
Richard III	1483-1485
Henry VII	1485-1509
Henry VIII	1509-1547
Edward VI	1547-1553
Mary	1553-1558
Elizabeth I	1558-1603
James I	1603-1625
Charles I	1625-1649
Commonwealth	1649-1660
Charles II	1660-1685
James II	1685-1689
William & Mary	1689-1694
William III	1694-1702
Anne	1702-1714
George I	1714-1727
George II	1727-1760
George III	1760-1820
George IV	1820-1830
William IV	1830-1837
Victoria	1837-1901
Edward VII	1901-1910

PERIODS

Jacobean	1603-1649
William & Mary	1689-1702
Queen Anne	1702-1714
Georgian	1714-1820
Chippendale	1750-1779
Adam	1762-1792
Hepplewhite	1780-1795
Sheraton	1790-1806
Regency	1795-1820
Victorian	1830-1901
Edwardian	1901-1910

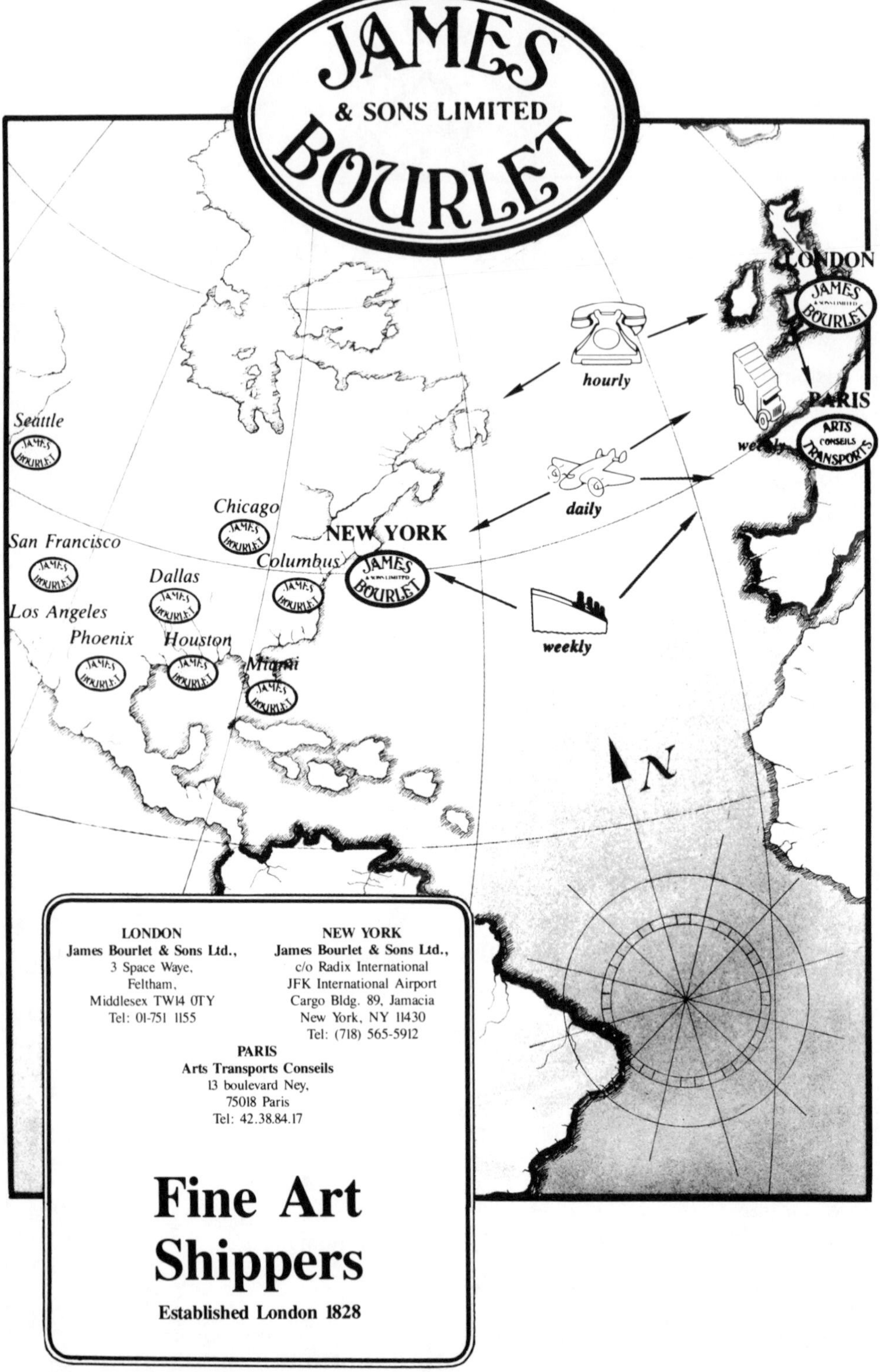

LONDON
James Bourlet & Sons Ltd.,
3 Space Waye,
Feltham,
Middlesex TW14 0TY
Tel: 01-751 1155

NEW YORK
James Bourlet & Sons Ltd.,
c/o Radix International
JFK International Airport
Cargo Bldg. 89, Jamacia
New York, NY 11430
Tel: (718) 565-5912

PARIS
Arts Transports Conseils
13 boulevard Ney,
75018 Paris
Tel: 42.38.84.17

Fine Art Shippers

Established London 1828

SHIPPERS AND PACKERS

JAMES BOURLET & SONS LTD.
3 Space Waye
Feltham
Middlesex TW14 OTY
Tel: 01 751 1155
Telex: 935242

DAVIES TURNER & CO. LTD.
334 Queenstown Road
London SW8 4NG
Tel: 01 622 4393
Telex: 8956479

FEATHERSTON SHIPPING LTD.
24 Hampton House
15-17 Ingate Place
London SW8 3NS
Tel: 01 720 0422
Telex: 9413290 Feship G.

C.R. FENTON & CO. LTD.
Beachy Road
Old Ford
London E3 2NX
Tel: 01 533 2711
Telex: Fenton G 8812859

GANDER & WHITE SHIPPING LTD.
21 Lillie Road
London SW6 1UE
Tel: 01 381 0571
Telex: 917434

HEDLEYS HUMPERS LTD.
157-159 Iverson Road
West Hampstead
London NW6 2RB
Tel: 01 625 4551
Telex: 25229

ANTIQUES TO SHIP?

For a quotation contact the specialists in packing, shipping and airfreighting of Antiques and Fine Art.

Ship your goods the safe, reliable, low cost way.

LAPADA Registered Member

FEATHERSTON SHIPPING LTD

24 Hampton House, 15-17 Ingate Place
London SW8 3NS
Tel: 01-720 0422   Telex: 9413290 Feship G

LOCKSON SERVICES LTD.
29 Broomfield Street
London E14 6BX
Tel: 01 515 8600
Telex: 884222

STEPHEN MORRIS SHIPPING LTD.
89 Upper Street
London N1 ONP
Tel: 01 354 1212
Telex: 261707

PITT & SCOTT LTD.
20-24 Eden Grove
London N7 8ED
Tel: 01 607 7321
Telex: 21857

L.J. ROBERTON LTD.
Marlborough House
Cooks Road, Stratford
London E15 2PW
Tel: 01 519 2020
Telex: 8953984

TRANS EURO
Drury Way, Brent Park
London NW10 OJM
Tel: 01 459 8080
Telex: 923368

WINGATE & JOHNSON LTD.
78 Broadway, Stratford
London E15 1NG
Tel: 01 555 8123
Telex: 897666

Early 18th century walnut corner chair.

AUCTIONEERS

BLOOMSBURY BOOK AUCTIONS
3-4 Hardwick Street, London, EC1R HRY..Tel: 01 833 2636
Sales of books, maps, prints and manuscripts. Approx. 20 sales per year.

BONHAMS
Montpelier Galleries, Montpelier Street,..Tel: 01 584 9161
Knightsbridge, London SW7 1HH..Telex: 916477 Bonham G
Fine art auctioneers selling a wide range of art and antiques. Catalogues are available at the galleries or by mail.

CAMDEN AUCTIONS
The Saleroom, Hoppers Road
Winchmore Hill, London N21..Tel: 01 886 1550
Sales on alternate Thursdays at 10.30 am. Viewing Wednesday 9.30-8.00, Thursday 9.00-10.30 am.

CHRISTIE'S
8 King Street, St. James's..Tel: 01 839 9060
London SW1Y 6QT..Telex: 916429
Fine art auctioneers.

CHRISTIE'S SOUTH KENSINGTON LTD.
85 Old Brompton Road, London SW7 3LD..Tel: 01 581 7611
....Telex: 922061
Sales of antique furniture, carpets, silver, jewelry, scientific instruments, ceramics textiles, toys, dolls, wines, postcards, prints.

GLENDINING AND CO.
Blenstock House, 7 Blenheim Street,
New Bond Street, London W1Y OAS..Tel: 01 493 2445
Sales of coins and military medals.

HARVEY'S AUCTIONS LTD.
14-18 Neal Street, London WC2H 9LZ..Tel. 01 240 1464
Sales of furniture, silver, paintings, ceramics, glass, carpets, prints, held weekly on Wednesday at 10.30 am. Viewing Tuesday 9.30 am-3:30 pm.

JACKSON-STOPS & STAFF
14 Curzon Street, London W1Y 7FH..Tel: 01 499 6291
Fine art auctioneers and valuers offering for sale the contents of private houses throughout Britain.

LONDON BRIDGE AUCTIONS
6 Park Street (off Stoney Street)
London Bridge, London SE1..Tel: 01 407 9577
Sales of furniture, silver, porcelain, clocks, watches, jewelry, prints, objets d'art, collectors items every Sunday at 2.00 pm. Viewing Sunday 10 am-2 pm.

LOTS ROAD GALLERIES
71 Lots Road, Chelsea, London SW10 ORN....................Tel: 01 351 5784 or 351 7771
Sales of selected furniture, ceramics, silver, paintings, clocks, books, Oriental carpets and rugs, held every Monday at 6.30 pm. Viewing Friday 9-4, Saturday & Sunday 10-1 and Monday 9-6.

PHILLIPS
Blenstock House. 7 Blenheim Street
New Bond Street, London W1Y OAS....................................Tel: 01 629 6602
Fine art auctioneers conducting sales of furniture, carpets, silver, ceramics, glass and many specialist sales.

PHILLIPS MARYLEBONE AUCTION ROOMS
Hayes Place, Lisson Grove, London NW1 6UA...........................Tel: 01 723 2647
Sales of furniture, paintings, ceramics etc. every Friday at 10 am. Viewing Thursdays.

PHILLIPS WEST 2
10 Salem Road, London W2 4BU...Tel: 01 221 5303
Sales of furniture, porcelain and objets d'art every Thursday at 10 am. Viewing Wednesdays.

SOTHEBY'S
34-35 New Bond Street, London W1A 2AA...............................Tel: 01 493 8080
....Telex: 24454 SPBLON G
Fine art auctioneers since 1744. Sales Monday-Friday.

SOUTHGATE ANTIQUE AUCTION ROOMS
Rear of Southgate Town Hall, Green Lanes
Palmer's Green, London N13...Tel: 01 886 7888
Sales of furniture, small antiques, jewelry every Friday at 6.30 pm. Viewing Friday 10 am-6.30 pm.

WALTHAM FOREST AUCTIONS LTD.
101 Hoe Street, Walthamstow, London E17..............................Tel: 01 520 2998
Sales of furniture, porcelain, silver, paintings, clocks, jewelry, rugs every Wednesday at 7 pm. Viewing 3 pm day of sale.

A pair of James II Scottish tankards by James Cockburn, Edinburgh, 1685.

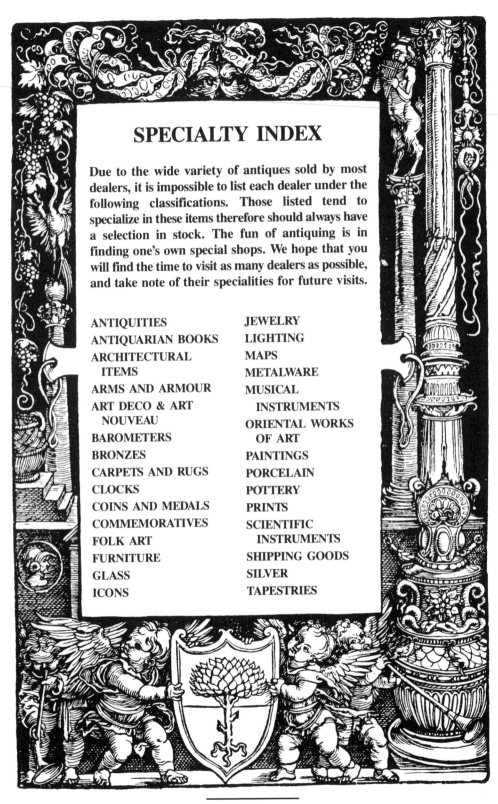

SPECIALTY INDEX

Due to the wide variety of antiques sold by most dealers, it is impossible to list each dealer under the following classifications. Those listed tend to specialize in these items therefore should always have a selection in stock. The fun of antiquing is in finding one's own special shops. We hope that you will find the time to visit as many dealers as possible, and take note of their specialities for future visits.

- ANTIQUITIES
- ANTIQUARIAN BOOKS
- ARCHITECTURAL ITEMS
- ARMS AND ARMOUR
- ART DECO & ART NOUVEAU
- BAROMETERS
- BRONZES
- CARPETS AND RUGS
- CLOCKS
- COINS AND MEDALS
- COMMEMORATIVES
- FOLK ART
- FURNITURE
- GLASS
- ICONS
- JEWELRY
- LIGHTING
- MAPS
- METALWARE
- MUSICAL INSTRUMENTS
- ORIENTAL WORKS OF ART
- PAINTINGS
- PORCELAIN
- POTTERY
- PRINTS
- SCIENTIFIC INSTRUMENTS
- SHIPPING GOODS
- SILVER
- TAPESTRIES

Antiquities

Aaron Gallery W.1.
Charles Ede Ltd. W.1.
McAlpine Ancient Art W.1.
Mansour Gallery W.1.
Robin Symes Ltd. S.W.1.

Antiquarian Books

Maggs Bros. Ltd. W.1.
Bernard Quaritch Ltd. W.1.
Chas J. Sawyer W.1.
Henry Sotheran Ltd. W.1.
World of Books W.1.
D. Mellor & A.L. Baxter W.8.
J. Allen & Co. S.W.1.
Cavendish Rare Books S.W.1.
Pickering & Chatto Ltd. S.W.1.
Thomas E. Schuster S.W.1.
Chelsea Rare Books S.W.3.
Harriet Wynter Ltd. S.W.10.
Vandeleur Antiquarian Books S.W.14.
Rogers Turner Books Ltd. S.E.10.
The Print Room W.C.1.
Skoob Books Ltd. W.C.1.
Anglebooks Ltd. W.C.2.
Clive A. Burden Ltd. W.C.2.
H.M. Fletcher W.C.2.
Frognal Rare Books W.C.2.
Reg & Philip Remington W.C.2.
Harold T. Storey W.C.2.
G.W. Walford N.1.
Keith Harding Antiques N.7.
Edna Whiteson Ltd. N.11.
M.E. Korn N.W.5.

Architectural Items

Crowther of Syon Lodge W.1.
T. Crowther & Son S.W.6.
Thornhill Galleries Ltd. S.W.6.
Thornhill Galleries Ltd. S.W.15.
Architectural Antiques Ltd. N.1.

Arms and Armour

Blunderbuss Antiques W.1.
Ronald A. Lee (Fine Arts) Ltd. W.1.
Michael German W.8.
Robert Hales Antiques Ltd. W.8.

Art Deco & Art Nouveau

Lewis M. Kaplan Associates Ltd. S.W.3.
Bizarre N.W.8.

Barometers

Grimaldi W.1.
E. Hollander S.W.3.
Patric Capon N.1.
Strike One Ltd. N.1.

Bronzes

J. Christie W.1.
The Sladmore Gallery W.1.
Claude Bornoff W.2.
Peter Nahum S.W.1.
Gerald Spyer & Son Ltd. S.W.1.

Carpets and Rugs

Avakian Oriental Carpets Ltd. W.1.
M. Heskia W.1.
C. John (Rare Rugs) Ltd. W.1.
Alexander Juran & Co. W.1.
Kennedy Carpets W.1.
Mayfair Carpet Gallery Ltd. W.1.
Portman Carpets W.1.
Vigo Carpet Gallery W.1.
Vigo-Sternberg Galleries W.1.
M.L. Waroujian W.6.
David Black Oriental Carpets W.11.
Jack Fairman (Carpets) Ltd. W.11.
Raymond Bernardout S.W.1.
S. Franses Ltd. S.W.1.
Victor Franses Gallery S.W.1.
Heraz S.W.1.
Mayorcas Ltd. S.W.1.
Atlantic Bay Carpets S.W.6.
Anglo-Persian Carpet Co. Ltd. S.W.7.
Benardout & Benardout S.W.7

J. Lavian N.W.5.
M. & M. Oriental Gallery Ltd. N.W.5.

Clocks

Asprey & Co. W.1.
N. Bloom & Sons Ltd. W.1.
Bobinet Ltd. W.1.
Carrington & Co. Ltd. W.1.
Garrard & Co. Ltd. W.1.
Grimaldi W.1.
Ronald A. Lee (Fine Arts)Ltd. W.1.
Mallett & Son (Antiques) Ltd. W.1.
Mallett at Bourdon House Ltd. W.1.
Bonrose Antiques W.8.
Philip & Bernard Dombey W.8.
Raffety W.8.
S. Lampard & Son Ltd. W.11.
Igor Tociapski W.11.
Camerer Cuss & Co. S.W.1.
John Carlton Smith S.W.1.
E. Hollander Ltd. S.W.3.
Big Ben Antique Clocks S.W.6.
Chelsea Clocks & Antiques S.W.6.
Aubrey Brocklehurst S.W.7.
Capital Clocks S.W.8.
The Clock Clinic Ltd. S.W.15.
Silver Sixpence S.E.6.
Asprey & Co. Ltd. E.C.3.
Bushe Antiques N.1.
Patric Capon N.1.
Strike One (Islington) Ltd. N.1.
North London Clock Shop N.5.
Keith Harding Antiques N.7.
Temple Brooks N.W.6.

Coins and Medals

B.A. Seaby Ltd. W.1.
Spink & Son Ltd. S.W.1.
A.H. Baldwin & Sons Ltd. W.C.2.

Commemoratives

Hope & Glory W.8.
J. & J. May W.8.

Folk Art

R.O. & F. Coyle W.8.
Crane Gallery S.W.1.
Robert Young Antiques S.W.11.

Furniture-Oak

Neptune Antiques W.1.
Antiquus A.G. W.2.
M. & D. Seligmann W.8.
Hirst Antiques W.11.
Louis Stanton W.11.
Anno Domino Antiques S.W.1.
Csaky's Antiques S.W.1.
Joanna Booth S.W.3.
Tony Bunzl & Zal Davar S.W.3.
David Alexander Antiques S.W.6.
Rendlesham & Dark S.W.10.
Robert Young Antiques S.W.11.
Simon Coleman S.W.13.
J. & R. Bateman Antiques S.W.15.
John Creed Antiques Ltd. N.1.
Heritage Antiques N.1.
This and That N.W.1.

Furniture-Georgian

Asprey & Co. W.1.
Bernheimer Fine Arts Ltd. W.1.
Brian Fielden W.1.
W.R. Harvey & Co. Ltd. W.1.
Hudson & Williams W.1.
Mallett & Son Ltd. W.1.
Kenneth Neame Ltd. W.1.
Stair & Co. W.1.
Peter Bentley W.2.
Claude Bornoff W.2.
Connaught Galleries W.2.
The Antique Home W.8.
Eddy Bardawil W.8.
Church Street Galleries Ltd. W.8.
Aubrey J. Coleman Antiques W.8.
Etna Antiques W.8.
C.H. Major (Antiques) Ltd. W.8.
Peel Antiques W.8.
Henry Phillips W.8.
M. & D. Seligmann W.8.

Sylvia Sheppard W.8.
Jacob Stodel W.8.
Murray Thomsom Ltd. W.8.
Fluss & Charlesworth Ltd. W.9.
Blake Antiques W.11.
Michael Davidson W.11.
George Johnson Antiques W.11.
J. Lipitch Ltd. W.11.
Didier Aaron (London) Ltd. S.W.1.
Anno Domino Antiques S.W.1.
Raymond Benardout S.W.1.
De Havilland (Antiques) Ltd. S.W.1.
Fernandes & Marche S.W.1.
General Trading Co. Ltd. S.W.1.
Ross Hamilton S.W.1.
Hotspur Ltd. S.W.1.
Richard Miles Antiques S.W.1.
Geoffrey Rose Ltd. S.W.1.
Gerald Spyer & Son Ltd. S.W.1.
Norman Adams Ltd. S.W.3.
Apter Fredericks Ltd. S.W.3.
H.C. Baxter & Sons S.W.3.
Philip Colleck Ltd. S.W.3.
Richard Courtney Ltd. S.W.3.
Robert Dickson Antiques S.W.3.
Michael Foster S.W.3.
C. Fredericks & Son S.W.3.
Godson & Coles S.W.3.
Anthony James & Son Ltd. S.W.3.
Jeremy Ltd. S.W.3.
Joan of Art Ltd. S.W.3.
John Keil Ltd. S.W.3.
Michael Lipitch S.W.3.
Pelham Galleries S.W.3.
David Pettifer Ltd. S.W.3.
David Tron Antiques S.W.3.
O.F. Wilson Ltd. S.W.3.
Clifford Wright Antiques Ltd. S.W.3.
Rocco D'Alessandro S.W.6.
Peter Francis W.C.1.
S. & H. Jewell W.C.2.
Dome Antiques (Exports) Ltd. N.1.
Kausmally Antiques N.1.
Stephen Orton Antiques N.1.
Vane House Antiques N.1.
Terry Antiques N.19.
W.R. Harvey & Co. Ltd. N.W.1.
Regent Antiques N.W.1.
Haverstock Antiques N.W.3.

Furniture-Victorian

Connaught Galleries W.2.
Haslam & Whiteway W.8.
P.R. Barham W.11.
Peter & Danielle Dodd W.11.
Krystyna Antiques W.11.
Rex Antiques W.11.
The Witch Ball W.11.
Zal Davar Antiques S.W.6.
M. Lassota S.W.6.
Ian Moggach Antiques S.W.6.
Furniture Cave S.W.10.
Tony Davis Inc. S.W.11.
Butchoff Antiques S.E.15.
Old Street Antiques E.C.1.
Bushwood Antiques N.1.
Stuart Martin N.6.
Chas L. Nyman & Co. Ltd. N.W.1.
Clive Daniel Antiques N.W.3.

Furniture-Pine

The Pine House W.2.
Stratton-Quinn Antiques Etc. W.4.
Adams Antiques S.W.6.
Anvil Interiors S.W.6.
C.W. Buckingham S.W.6.
Richard Morris Antiques S.W.6.
The Pine Mine S.W.6.
The Pine Village S.W.6.
Savile Pine S.W.6.
Nicholas Beech S.W.8.
Gothic Cottage Antiques S.W.13.
Remember When S.W.13.
Wimbledon Pine Mine S.W.19.
Scallywag S.E.5.
Silver Sixpence S.E.6.
John Creed Antiques Ltd. N.1.
Geranium N.1.
Michael Lewis Antiques N.1.
The Shop on the Corner N.1.
Princedale Antiques N.7.
Adams Antiques N.W.1.
Country Pine N.W.1.

Glass

Arenski W.1.

Thomas Goode & Co. W.1.
Jeanette Hayhurst W.1.
Howard Phillips W.1.
Gerald Sattin Ltd. W.1.
Delomosne & Son Ltd. W.8.
Mercury Antiques W.11.
W.G.T. Burne Ltd. S.W.3.
Mark J. West-Cobb Antiques Ltd. S.W.19.
Mark J. West-Cobb Antiques Ltd. N.1.

Icons

Mark Gallery W.2.
The Winter Palace W.8.
Axia W.11.
Iconastas S.W.1.
Maria Andipa S.W.3.
Temple Gallery S.W.3.

Jewelry

Philip Antrobus W.1.
Armour-Winston Ltd. W.1.
Asprey & Co. W.1.
Bentley & Co. Ltd. W.1.
Anne Bloom W.1.
N. Bloom & Sons Ltd. W.1.
Bruford & Heming Ltd. W.1.
Carrington & Co Ltd. W.1.
Collingwood of Conduit Street W.1.
A.B. Davis Ltd. W.1.
Demas W.1.
Denisa The Lady Newborough W.1.
Garrard & Co. Ltd. W.1.
The Golden Post W.1.
Graus Antiques W.1.
M. Hakim W.1.
Hancocks & Co. Ltd. W.1.
Nicholas Harris W.1.
Harvey & Gore (Antiques) Ltd. W.1.
Hennel Ltd. W.1.
Holmes Ltd. W.1.
The Jewel House W.1.
Johnson, Walker & Tolhurst Ltd. W.1.
D.S. Lavender Antiques Ltd. W.1.
Massada Antiques W.1.
Nigel Milne Ltd. W.1.
L. Newland & Son W.1.
Richard Ogden Ltd. W.1.
S.J. Phillips Ltd. W.1.
Simeon W.1.
Tessiers Ltd. W.1.
Wartski Ltd. W.1.
"Young Stephen" Ltd. W.1.
A.B. Davis Ltd. W.2.
M. McAleer W.2.
Lev (Antiques) Ltd. W.8.
S. Lampard & Son Ltd. W.11.
Maurice Asprey Ltd. S.W.1.
Cornucopia S.W.1.
M. Ekstein Ltd. S.W.1.
Paul Longmire Ltd. S.W.1.
Spink & Son Ltd. S.W.1.
Louise Stroud S.W.3.
Whitworth & O'Donnell Ltd. S.E.13.
Essie C. Harris E.C.1.
Priory Antiques E.C.1.
A.R. Ullmann Ltd. E.C.1.
Asprey & Co. Ltd. E.C.3.
Searle & Co. Ltd. E.C.3.
J.I. Horwit W.C.1.
Shapland W.C.1.
Pearl Cross Ltd. W.C.2.
The Silver Mouse Trap W.C.2.
Inheritance N.1.
The Corner Cupboard N.W.2.
The Trinket Box N.W.6.

Lighting

N. Davighi W.6.
Mrs. M.E. Crick Ltd. W.8.
David Malik & Son W.8.
Christopher Wray S.W.6.
The Lighthouse Ltd. S.W.19.
End of Day N.W.6.

Maps

Jonathan Potter Ltd. W.1.
Tooley Adams & Co. Ltd. W.1.
O'Shea Gallery S.W.1.
Thomas E. Schuster S.W.1.
The Map House S.W.3.
Cartographia Ltd. W.C.1.
Robert Douwma Ltd. W.C.2.
Avril Noble W.C.2.

Metalware

The Curio Shop W.1.
Jack Casimir Ltd. W.11.
Rod's Antiques W.11.
Alistair Sampson S.W.3.
Christopher Bangs S.W.11.
John Creed Antiques Ltd. N.1.
Gordon Gridley N.1.
Heritage Antiques N.1.

Musical Instruments

J. & A. Beare Ltd. W.1.
Tony Bingham N.W.3.

Oriental Works of Art

Barling of Mount Street W.1.
Bluett & Sons Ltd. W.1.
Eskenazi Ltd. W.1.
Thomas Goode & Co. W.1.
Sydney L. Moss Ltd. W.1.
John Sparks Ltd. W.1.
A. & J. Speelman W.1.
Cathay Antiques W.8.
Peter Kemp W.8.
S. Marchant & Son W.8.
D.C. Monk & Son W.8.
Jacob Stodel W.8.
Helen Buxton Antiques W.11.
Cohen & Pearce W.11.
Ormonde Gallery W.11.
R. & D. Coombes W.14.
Belgravia Gallery S.W.1.
Ciancimino S.W.1.
Robert Hall S.W.1.
Tempus Antiques Ltd. S.W.1.
David Tremayne Ltd. S.W.3.
David Alexander Antiques S.W.6.
Chancery Antiques Ltd. N.1.
Hart & Rosenberg N.1.
Japanese Gallery N.1.
Wan Li N.1.
Magus Antiques N.W.8.

Paintings

Arthur Ackermann & Son Ltd. W.1.
Thomas Agnew & Sons Ltd. W.1.
Burlington Paintings Ltd. W.1.
Clarendon Gallery W.1.
P. & D. Colnaghi & Co. Ltd. W.1.
The Fine Art Society W.1.
Frost & Reed Ltd. W.1.
Christopher Gibbs Ltd. W.1.
Thomas Gibson Fine Art Ltd. W.1.
Richard Green W.1.
Hahn & Son Fine Art Dealers W.1.
The Leger Galleries Ltd. W.1.
Maas Gallery W.1.
MacConnal Mason Gallery W.1.
John Mitchell & Son W.1.
The Parker Gallery W.1.
W.H. Patterson Fine Arts Ltd. W.1.
Anthony Reed W.1.
Somerville & Simpson W.1.
Edward Speelman Ltd. W.1.
H.J. Spiller Ltd. W.1.
Williams & Son W.1.
Ealing Gallery W.5.
Baumkotter Gallery W.8.
R. & J. Jones W.8.
Little Winchester Gallery W.8.
Albion Fine Art W.11.
Caelt Gallery W.11.
Gavin Graham Gallery W.11.
Lacy Gallery W.11.
Addison-Ross Gallery S.W.1.
Albany Gallery S.W.1.
Appleby Bros. Ltd. S.W.1.
Artemis Fine Art (U.K.) Ltd. S.W.1.
Chris Beetles Ltd. S.W.1.
Chaucer Fine Arts Inc. S.W.1.
Douwes Fine Art S.W.1.
Owen Edgar Gallery S.W.1.
Fry Gallery S.W.1.
Harari & Johns Ltd. S.W.1.
Hazlitt, Gooden & Fox Ltd. S.W.1.
Heim Gallery S.W.1.
Alan Jacobs Gallery S.W.1.
Oscar & Peter Johnson Ltd. S.W.1.
David Ker Fine Art S.W.1.
King Street Galleries S.W.1.
Lane Fine Art Ltd. S.W.1.
Lasson Gallery S.W.1.
Leggatt Brothers S.W.1.
MacConnal Mason Gallery S.W.1.
Paul Mason S.W.1.

Mathaf Gallery Ltd. S.W.1.
Peter Nahum S.W.1.
Omel Galleries S.W.1.
Pawsey & Payne S.W.1.
Polak Gallery S.W.1.
Pyms Gallery S.W.1.
Johnny Van Haeften Ltd. S.W.1.
Christopher Wood Gallery S.W.1.
Stephen Garratt S.W.3.
David James Fine Paintings S.W.3.
Fleur de Lys Gallery S.W.6.
Paisnel Gallery Ltd. S.W.6.
Royal Exchange Art Gallery E.C.3.
Swan Fine Art N.1.
Leigh Underhill Gallery N.1.
Lauri Stewart-Fine Art N.2.
Park Galleries N.3.
Centaur Gallery N.6.
Highgate Gallery N.6.
John Denham Gallery N.W.6.
The Bank House Gallery N.W.7.
Wellington Gallery N.W.8.

Porcelain

Adams W.1.
Antique Porcelain Co. Ltd. W.1.
Bernheimer Fine Arts Ltd. W.1.
Thomas Goode & Co. W.1.
Brian Haughton Antiques W.1.
Heirloom & Howard Ltd. W.1.
D.M. & P. Manheim Ltd. W.1.
David Brower Antiques W.8.
Belinda Coote Antiques W.8.
Davies Antiques W.8.
Delomosne & Son Ltd. W.8.
H. & W. Deutsch Antiques W.8.
Graham & Oxley Ltd. W.8.
Grosvenor Antiques Ltd. W.8.
Hoff Antiques W.8.
R. & J. Jones W.8.
Peter Kemp W.8.
Klaber & Klaber W.8.
Eric Lineham & Sons W.8.
J. & J. May W.8.
D.C. Monk & Son W.8.
St. Jude's Antiques W.8.
Jean Sewell (Antiques) Ltd. W.8.
Mary Wise W.8.
Edward Salti W.9.
Mercury Antiques W.11.
Albert Amor Ltd. S.W.1.
Bayly's Gallery Antiques S.W.1.
Kate Foster Ltd. S.W.1.
Winifred Williams S.W.1.
H.H. Newby S.W.3.
Earle D. Vandekar S.W.3.
Susan Becker Antiques S.W.15.
Chancery Antiques N.1.
Gerald Clark Antiques Ltd. N.W.7.

Pottery

Brian Haughton Antiques W.1.
D.M. & P. Manheim Ltd. W.1.
Venners Antiques W.1.
Anthony Belton W.8.
Belinda Coote Antiques W.8.
Richard Dennis W.8.
Graham & Oxley Ltd. W.8.
Jonathan Horne W.8.
Lindsay Antiques W.8.
J. & J. May W.8.
Oliver-Sutton Antiques W.8.
Arthur Seager Antiques Ltd. W.8.
M. & D. Seligmann W.8.
Jean Sewell (Antiques) Ltd. W.8.
Constance Stobo W.8.
Mercury Antiques W.11.
Ledger Antiques S.W.3.
Alistair Sampson Antiques S.W.3.
Earle D. Vandekar S.W.3.
Gerald Clark Antiques Ltd. N.W.7.

Prints

Arthur Ackermann & Son Ltd. W.1.
Burlington Gallery Ltd. W.1.
Lumley Cazalet Ltd. W.1.
The Parker Gallery W.1.
Jonathan Potter Ltd. W.1.
Henry Sotheran Ltd. W.1.
Tooley Adams & Co. Ltd. W.1.
Davies Antiques W.8.
D. Mellor & A.L. Baxter W.8.
John Reid W.8.
Lacy Gallery W.11.

Raymond O'Shea S.W.1.
Thomas E. Schuster S.W.1.
Stephanie Hoppen Ltd. S.W.3.
Vandeleur Antiquarian Books S.W.14.
The Print Room W.C.1.
Clive A. Burden Ltd. W.C.2.
Cartographia W.C.1.
Robert Douwma W.C.2.
Grosvenor Prints W.C.2.
John Denham Gallery N.W.6.

Scientific Instruments

Mayfair Microscopes Ltd. W.1.
Rod's Antiques W.11.
Arthur Davidson Ltd. S.W.1.
David Weston Ltd. S.W.1.
Harriet Wynter Ltd. S.W.10.
Vintage Cameras Ltd. S.E.26.
Langfords Galleries W.C.2.
Arthur Middleton Ltd. W.C.2.

Shipping Goods

Bermondsey Antique Warehouse S.E.1.
Lamont Antiques Ltd. S.E.1.
MacNeill's Art & Antique Warehouse S.E.1.
Oola Boola Antiques S.E.1.
Tower Bridge Antique Warehouse S.E.1.
Ian Wilson Antiques S.E.15.
Ages Ago S.E.26.
J.C. Antiques E.17.
Garrick House Antiques N.1.
M. & S. Antiques N.16.
Ian Crispin Antiques N.W.1.

Silver

A.D.C. Heritage Ltd. W.1.
Armitage W.1.
Asprey & Co. W.1.
Paul Bennett W.1.
Anne Bloom W.1.
N. Bloom & Sons Ltd. W.1.
Bond Street Silver Galleries W.1.
Bruford & Heming Ltd. W.1.
Peter Cameron W.1.
Carrington & Co. Ltd. W.1.
J. Christie W.1.
Collingwood of Conduit Street W.1.
A.B. Davis Ltd. W.1.
Denisa the Lady Newborough W.1.
Garrard & Co. Ltd. W.1.
The Golden Past W.1.
Simon Griffin Antiques W.1.
Hancocks & Co. W.1.
Harris (Antiques) Ltd. W.1.
Nicholas Harris W.1.
Harvey & Gore (Antiques) Ltd. W.1.
Hennell Ltd. W.1.
Holmes Ltd. W.1.
Johnson, Walker & Tolhurst Ltd. W.1.
D.S. Lavender Antiques Ltd. W.1.
M. & L. Silver Co. Ltd. W.1.
Marks Antiques Ltd. W.1.
Massada Antiques W.1.
Nigel Milne Ltd. W.1.
Richard Ogden Ltd. W.1.
S.J. Phillips Ltd. W.1.
David Richards & Sons W.1.
Gerald Sattin Ltd. W.1.
Tessiers Ltd. W.1.
Wartski Ltd. W.1.
Henry Willis W.1.
A.B. Davis Ltd. W.2.
M. McAleer W.2.
H. & W. Deutsch Antiques W.8.
Howard Jones W.8.
Lev (Antiques) Ltd. W.8.
J. Freeman W.11.
Hyde Park Antiques W.11.
S. Lampard & Son Ltd. W.11.
London International Silver Co. Ltd. W.11.
Portobello Silver Co. W.11.
Maurice Asprey Ltd. S.W.1.
J.H. Bourdon-Smith Ltd. S.W.1.
Mary Cooke Antiques S.W.1.
DeHavilland (Antiques) Ltd. S.W.1.
M. Ekstein Ltd. S.W.1.
How of Edinburgh S.W.1.
Brand Inglis Ltd. S.W.1.
H.R. Jessop Ltd. S.W.1.
Paul Longmire Ltd. S.W.1.
Spink & Son Ltd. S.W.1.
E. Hollander Ltd. S.W.3.
Stanley Leslie S.W.3.
Sanda Lipton S.W.5.

M.P. Levene Ltd. S.W.7.
A.R. Ullmann Ltd. E.C.1.
C.J. Vander (Antiques) Ltd. E.C.1.
Asprey & Co. Ltd. E.C.3.
Searle & Co. Ltd. E.C.3.
Shapland W.C.1.
S.J. Shrubsole Ltd. W.C.1.
The London Silver Vaults W.C.2.
Pearl Cross Ltd. W.C.2.
H. Perovetz Ltd. W.C.2.
The Silver Mouse Trap W.C.2.
David Graham Antiques N.1.
Heather Antiques N.1.
John Laurie Antiques Ltd. N.1.
Stanley Beal Ltd. N.W.6.

Tapestries

C. John (Rare Rugs) Ltd. W.1.
Alexander Juran & Co. W.1.
Vigo-Sternberg Galleries W.1.
Antiquus A.G. W.2.
Belinda Coote Antiques W.8.
S. Franses Ltd. S.W.1.
Victor Franses Gallery S.W.1.
Mayorcas Ltd. S.W.1.
Pelham Galleries S.W.3.
J. Lavian N.W.5.

Charles VII on horseback
by
Antoine Louis Barye

ALPHABETICAL LIST OF DEALERS

Black Oriental Carpets, David-W.11.
Blairman and Sons Ltd., H-W.1.
Blake Antiques-W.11.
Bloom Anne-W.1.
Bloom & Son (Antiques) Ltd., N.-W.1.
Bluett and Sons Ltd.,-W.1.
Blunderbuss Antiques-W.1.
Bobinet Ltd.-W.1.
Bond Street Antique Centre-W.1.
Bond Street Silver Galleries-W.1.
Bonnett, R.-S.W.6.
Bonrose Antiques-W.8.
Bookham Galleries-S.W.6.
Booth, Joanna-S.W.3.
Bornoff, Claude-W.2.
Bourdon-Smith Ltd., J.H.-S.W.1.
Box House Antiques-S.W.1.
Braham Ltd., Maurice-W.8.
Briggs Ltd., F.E.A.-W.11.
Brocantiques-N.W.10.
Brocklehurst, Aubrey-S.W.7.
Brook Antiques, Beverley-S.W.13.
Brooks, Temple-N.W.5.
Brower Antiques, David-W.8.
Brown I. & J.L.-S.W.6.
Bruford and Heming Ltd.-W.1.
Buck & Payne Antiques-N.1.
Buckingham, C.W.-S.W.6.
Bunzl, Tony & Zal Davar-S.W.3.
Burden Ltd., Clive A.-W.C.2.
Burlington Gallery Ltd.-W.1.
Burlington Paintings Ltd.-W.1.
Burne (Antique Glass) Ltd., W.G.T.-S.W.3.
Bushe Antiques-N.1.
Bushwood Antiques-N.1.
Butchoff Antiques-S.E.15.
Buxton Antiques, Helen-W.11.

C

Caelt Gallery-W.11.
Camden Antiques Trade Market-N.W.1.
Camden Lock Antiques Centre, The-N.W.1.
Camden Passage Antiques Centre-N.1.
Camerer Cuss and Co.-S.W.1.
Cameron, Peter-W.1.
Campbell Picture Frames Ltd., John-S.W.3.
Canonbury Antiques-N.1
Canonbury Antiques Ltd.-W.11.
Capital Clocks-S.W.8.
Capon, Patric-N.1.
Capricorn Antiques-N.1.
Carleton, Michael-N.W.3.
Carrington and Co. Ltd.-W.1.
Carthew, Olwen-S.E.26.
Cartographia Ltd.-W.C.1.
Casimir Ltd., Jack-W.11.
Cassio Antiques-W.11.
Castle, Simon-W.8.
Cathay Antiques-W.8.
Cavendish Rare Books-S.W.1.
Cavendish Antiques, Rupert-S.W.6.
Cazalet Ltd., Lumley-W.1.
Centaur Gallery-N.6.
Chancery Antiques Ltd.-N.1.
Chanteau-S.W.10.
Chapman and Davies Antiques-N.1.
Chaucer Fine Arts Inc.-S.W.1.
Chelsea Antique Market-S.W.3.
Chelsea Bric-a-Brac Shop Ltd.-S.W.19.
Chelsea Clocks and Antiques-S.W.6.
Chelsea Rare Books-S.W.3.
Chenil Galleries-S.W.3.
Chiswick Antiques-W.4.
Chiswick Fireplaces-W.4.
Christie, J.-W.1.
Church St. Antiques-N.W.8.
Church Street Galleries Ltd.-W.8.
Ciancimino Ltd.-S.W.1.
Clarendon Gallery-W.1.
Clark Antiques Ltd., Gerald-N.W.7.
Clay, John-S.W.6.
Clock Clinic Ltd., The-S.W.15.
Clunes Antiques-S.W.19.
Cochrane Antiques, Fergus-S.W.6.
Cocozza Antiques-W.11.
Cohen and Pearce-W.11.
Colefax and Fowler-W.1.
Coleman Antiques, Aubrey J.-W.8.
Coleman Antiques, Simon-S.W.13.
Colleck Ltd., Philip-S.W.3.
Collingwood of Conduit Street-W.1.
Collins Antiques, Frank-W.11.
Colnaghi-W.1.
Connaught Galleries-W.2.
Cook and Son, S.A.-N.W.3.
Cooke Antiques Ltd., Mary-S.W.1.
Coombes, R. and D.-W.14.
Coote Antiques, Belinda-W.8.
Corner Cupboard, The-N.W.2.
Corner Portobello Antiques Supermarket-W.11.
Cornucopia-S.W.1.
Country Pine-N.W.1.
Courtney Ltd., Richard-S.W.3.
Covent Garden Flea Market-W.C.2.
Coyle, R.O. & F.-W.8.
Crane Gallery-S.W.1.
Creed Antiques Ltd., John-N.1.
Crest Antiques-S.W.15.
Crick Ltd., Mrs. M.E.-W.8.
Crispin Antiques, Ian-N.W.1.

Crowther of Syon Lodge-W.1.
Crowther and Son Ltd., T.-S.W.6.
Csaky's Antiques-S.W.1.
Curio Shop, The-W.1.

D

Dale, John-W.11.
D'Allesandro, Rocco-S.W.6.
Daniel Antiques, Clive-N.W.3.
Davar, Zal-S.W.6.
Davidson Ltd., Arthur-S.W.1.
Davidson, Michael-W.11.
Davies Antiques-W.8.
Davighi, N.-W.6.
Davis Ltd., A.B.-W.1.
Davis Ltd., A.B.-W.2.
Davis Inc., Tony-S.W.11.
Davis, Kenneth-S.W.1.
De Havilland (Antiques) Ltd.-S.W.1.
Delomosne and Son Ltd.-W.8.
Demas-W.1.
Den of Antiquity-S.W.20.
Denham Gallery, John-N.W.6.
Denisa, The Lady Newborough-W.1.
Dennis, Richard-W.8.
Denton Antiques-S.E.26.
Deutsch Antiques, H. and W.-W.8.
Dickson Antiques, Robert-S.W.3.
Diddy Box, The-N.W.6.
Dixon's Antique Market-S.W.14.
Dodd, Peter and Daniele-W.11.
Dodo Old Advertising-W.11.
Dolls House Toys Ltd., The-W.C.2.
Dombey, Philip and Bernard-W.8.
Dome Antiques (Exports) Ltd.-N.1.
Donay Antiques-N.1.
Douwes Fine Art-S.W.1.
Douwma Ltd., Robert-W.C.2.

E

E. and A. Antiques-W.11.
Ealing Gallery-W.5.
Ede Ltd., Charles-W.1.
Edgar Gallery, Owen-S.W.1.
Edwards, Martin-W.11.
Ekstein Ltd., M.-S.W.1.
Eldridge London & Co.-E.C.1.
Elgin Antiques-W.11.
Ellis Antiques, Tony-N.5.
Emanouel Antiques Ltd.-W.1.
End of Day-N.W.6.
Eskenazi Ltd.-W.1.
Ester Antiques-N.5.
Etna Antiques-W.8.
Evanson, P.-S.W.6.
Ewing, J.F.-S.W.19.

F

Facade, The-W.11.
Fairman (Carpets) Ltd., Jack-W.11.
Farrelly, S.-S.W.16.
Farrelly, Stephen-N.W.3.
Fernandes and Marche-S.W.1.
Ferrant Antiques, D.J.-N.1.
Fielden, Brian-W.1.
Finch, Keith-W.11.
Finchley Fine Art Galleries-N.12.
Fine Art Society, The-W.1.
Five Five Six Antiques-S.W.6.
Fleamarket, The-N.1.
Fletcher, H.M.-W.C.2.
Fleur de Lys Gallery-S.W.6.
Floyd Ltd., George-S.W.6.
Fluss and Charlesworth Ltd.-W.9.
Foster Ltd., Kate-S.W.1.
Foster, Michael-S.W.3.
Foster of Putney-S.W.15.
Fowle, A. and J.,-S.W.16.
Fox, Judy-W.11.
Francis, Peter-W.C.1.
Franco's Antique Warehouse-N.1.
Franklin's Camberwell Antique Market-S.E.5.
Franses Ltd., S.-S.W.1.
Franses Gallery, Victor-S.W.1.
Fredericks and Son, C.-S.W.3.
Freeman and Son, I., Simon Kaye Ltd.-W.1.
Freeman, J.-W.11.
Freeman, Vincent-N.1.
Frognal Rare Books-W.C.2.
Frost and Reed Ltd.-W.1.
Fry Gallery-S.W.1.
Furniture Cave-S.W.10.
Furniture Fair-N.W.8.
Furniture Vault-N.1.

G

Galerie 1900-N.W.1.
Gallery '25-S.W.1.
Gallery of Antique Costume & Textiles-N.W.8.
Garrard and Co. Ltd.-W.1.
Garratt (Fine Paintings), Stephen-S.W.3.
Garrick House Antiques-N.1.
General Trading Co. Ltd.-S.W.1.
Georgian Village-N.1.
Georgian Village Antiques Market-E.17.
Geranium-N.1.
German, Michael C.-W.8.
Gibbs Ltd., Christopher-W.1.
Gibson Fine Art Ltd., Thomas-W.1.
Gillingham Ltd., G. and F.-N.W.6.
Godson and Coles-S.W.3.
Golden Past, The-W.1.

K

L

M

Mercury Antiques-W.11.
Messim, S.-W.11.
Middleton Ltd., Arthur-W.C.2.
Miles Antiques, Richard-S.W.1.
Milne Ltd., Nigel-W.1.
Mitchell & Son, John-W.1.
Mitchell Antiques, Lawrence-N.1.
Mitchell, Paul-W.1.
Moggach, Ian-S.W.6.
Money (Antiques) Ltd., Lennox-S.W.1.
Monk and Son, D.C.-W.8.
Morris Antiques, Richard-S.W.6.
Mortlake Antiques-S.W.14.
Moss Ltd., Sydney L.-W.1.
Mount Street Galleries-W.1.
Mundy, Richard-W.1.
Myers (Autographs) Ltd., W.A.-W.C.2.

N

Nahum, Peter-S.W.1.
Napier Ltd., Sylvia-W.11.
Neame Ltd., Kenneth-W.1.
Neptune Antiques-W.1.
New Cutler Street Antiques Market, The-E.1.
Newby, H.W.-S.W.3.
Newland & Son, L.-W.1.
Noble, Avril-W.C.2.
North London Clock Shop Ltd.-N.5.
Number 6 Antiques-N.W.8.
Nyman and Co. Ltd., Chas. L.-N.W.1.

O

Ogden Ltd., Richard-W.1.
Old Curiosity Shop-W.C.2.
Old Stables Market, The-N.W.1.
Old Street Antiques-E.C.1.
Old World Trading Co.-S.W.6.
Oliver-Sutton Antiques-W.8.
Omell Galleries-S.W.1.
Oola Boola Antiques-S.E.1.
Ormonde Gallery-W.11.
Orton Antiques, Stephen-N.1.
O'Shea Gallery-S.W.1.

P

Page Antiques, Kevin A.-N.1.
Paisnel Gallery Ltd.-S.W.6.
Park Galleries-N.3.
Parker Gallery, The-W.1.
Parker Antiques, Michael & Margaret-S.W.7.
Partridge Fine Arts Ltd.-W.1.
Patterson Fine Arts Ltd., W.H.-W.1.
Pawsey and Payne-S.W.1.
Pearl Cross Ltd.-W.C.2.
Peckham Rye Antiques-S.E.15.
Peel Antiques-W.8.
Pelham Galleries-S.W.3.
Penny Farthing Antiques Arcade-S.E.1.
Perovetz Ltd., H.-W.C.2.
Persian Market-N.1.
Pettifer Ltd., David-S.W.3.
Phelps, Michael-S.W.15.
Phillips and Sons, E.S.-W.11.
Phillips, Henry-W.8.
Phillips, Howard-W.1.
Phillips Ltd., Ronald-W.1.
Phillips Ltd., S.J.-W.1.
Philp, Richard-W.11.
Pickering & Chatto Ltd.-S.W.1.
Pine House, The-W.2.
Pine Mine, The-S.W.6.
Pine Village, The-S.W.6.
Polak Gallery-S.W.1.
Polly, A.-S.E.10.
Pope & Hunts Antiques Ltd., John-S.W.7.
Portman Carpets-W.1.
Portmeirion Antiques-S.W.13.
Portobello Silver Co.-W.11.
Potter Ltd., Jonathan-W.1.
Poulter and Son, H.W.-S.W.10.
Princedale Antiques-N.7.
Princedale Antiques-W.11.
Print Room, The-W.C.1.
Priory Antiques-E.C.1.
Putnams Kitchen Antiques-N.W.6.
Pym Gallery-S.W.1.

Q

Quaritch Ltd., Bernard-W.1.
Quest Antiques-W.13.
Questor Antiques-W.6.
Quinn Antiques, Barrie-S.W.6.

R

Rabi Gallery-W.1.
Raffety-W.8.
Randalls Antiques-S.W.13.
Raphael, A.-W.11.
Redford, William-W.1.
Redmile Ltd., J.A.-S.W.1.
Reed, Anthony-W.1.
Regent Antiques-N.W.1.
Reid, John-W.8.
Relcy Antiques-S.E.10.
Remember When-S.W.13.
Remington, Reg & Philip-W.C.2.
Rendall Antiques-S.W.6.
Rendlesham and Dark-S.W.10.
Rex Antiques-W.11.

S

T

U

V

W

Y

Early Ch'ien Lung enamel centerpiece.

Where to stay

It would be impossible for us to give a complete account of all the accommodations available, but we hope this section will give some idea of the broad range of hotels, mainly in the central area.

Price categories are denoted by the number of $'s and signify the approximate price of a double room with breakfast. If hotel reservations are made as part of a 'package deal' the room rates may be considerably less.

$	under $50	$$$	$100-$140
$$	$50-$100	$$$$	over $140

W.1. Hotels

$$$$ **BROWNS HOTEL**
21-24 Dover Street
Tel: 493 6020
Telex: 28686
Very traditional hotel dating back to 1837. Popular with Americans, all 126 rooms have bath or shower. Restaurant and bar.

$$$$ **CHURCHILL**
30 Portman Square
Tel: 486 5800
Telex: 264831
Very large, very popular West End hotel. Number Ten Dining Room, Greenery Coffee Shop, Regency Lounge and bar. Garage.

$$$$ **CLARIDGES**
Brook Street
Tel: 629 8860
Telex: 21872
This elegant hotel, situated in fashionable Mayfair, is a favorite with visiting Royalty. 205 rooms all with baths. Restaurant and lounge. Garage.

$$$$ **CONNAUGHT**
16 Carlos Place
Tel: 499 7070
Elegant, traditional hotel between Berkeley and Grosvenor Squares. 89 rooms all with baths. It boasts one of the finest restaurants in London.

$$$$ **DORCHESTER**
Park Lane
Tel: 629 8888
Telex: 887704
Excellent, stylish hotel overlooking Hyde Park. A favorite with celebrities. Private library for guests. Recently refurbished, all 290 rooms with bath or shower. Service excellent. French restaurant, Grill, lounge and bar. Garage.

$$$$ **GROSVENOR HOUSE**
Park Lane
Tel: 499 6363
Telex: 24871
Superior deluxe hotel overlooking Hyde Park. 478 rooms all with baths. Health club featuring swimming pool, sauna and gymnasium. Three restaurants, lounge and cocktail bars. Garage.

$$$$ **INN ON THE PARK**
Hamilton Place
Park Lane
Tel: 499 0888
Telex: 22771
Luxury hotel at south end of Park Lane. 228 rooms all with private bath. Four Seasons restaurant - large menu at reasonable prices.

$$$ **THE LADBROKE CURZON**
2 Stanhope Row
Park Lane
Tel: 493 7222
Telex: 24665
Small first-class Georgian hotel in exclusive Mayfair area. All 71 rooms with color T.V. and showers. Coffee-shop restaurant.

$$$$ **LE MERIDIEN**
Piccadilly
Tel: 734 8000
Telex: 25795
Reopened in 1985 after extensive refurbishing, this 290 room hotel has it all. Air-conditioned rooms with direct-dial telephone, television with in-house movie system, minibar and trouser press. The Health Club features swimming pool, Nautilus gymnasium, Turkish baths, jacuzzi, squash courts and billiard room. The Oak Room features gourmet dining under the direction of Chef David Chambers. Very expensive but very luxurious.

$$$$ **LONDON MARRIOTT**
Grosvenor Square
Tel: 493 1232
Telex: 268101
Superior deluxe hotel opposite the U.S. Embassy. Formerly the Europa, this hotel offers rooms with full bath and shower, direct-dial telephone, color T.V. and mini-bar. International restaurant, coffee shop, lounge and bar.

$$$ **PARK LANE**
Piccadilly
Tel: 499 6321
Telex: 21533
Superior first-class hotel in Mayfair. Large rooms all with color T.V., telephone and mini-bar. Restaurant, coffee shop and bar.

$$$$ **RITZ**
Piccadilly
Tel: 493 8181
Telex: 267200
Elegant hotel with fine restaurant in Louis XV sytle. Palm-court lounge - just the place for afternoon tea. Bar and casino.

W.1.

$$$ **THE SAVOY COURT**
Granville Place
W.1.
Tel: 408 0130 U.S. 800 447 7011
Telex: 8955515
Tucked away in a quiet mews behind Oxford Street. All rooms with private bathroom, color T.V., direct-dial telephone. Restaurant and bar.

$$$$ **THE SELFRIDGE HOTEL**
400 Orchard Street
Tel: 408 2080
Telex: 22361
This deluxe hotel with it's old English charm, is centrally located in the heart of the West End. Fletcher's Restaurant offers international cuisine, Stoves Bar is charming, there is also a coffee shop. All rooms are air-conditioned.

$$ **SHERLOCK HOLMES**
108 Baker Street
Tel: 486 6161,
Telex: 8954837
This Regency-style tourist hotel is within easy walking distance of Oxford Street. 153 rooms, all with private bathroom and color T.V. Italian restaurant, several lounges and bar.

$$$ **THE WASHINGTON HOTEL**
Curzon Street, Mayfair
Tel: 499 7030
Telex: 24540
Pleasant centrally located hotel in the heart of Mayfair. 160 rooms, each with bath/shower, phone and television. Car parking can be a problem.

$$$$ **WESTBURY**
New Bond Street
Tel: 629 7755
Telex: 24378
Centrally located, comfortable hotel. All rooms with bath. Nouvelle cuisine restaurant and bar.

W.2. Hotels

$ **ABBEY COURT HOTEL**
174 Sussex Gardens
Tel: 402 0704
This bed and breakfast hotel is close to Lancaster Gate underground station. Most rooms have private shower.

$$ **CHARLES DICKENS**
66 Lancaster Gate
Tel: 262 5090
Telex: 27120
Traditional tourist-class hotel close to Hyde Park and Marble Arch. Comfortable rooms, all with private bathroom and color T.V. Oliver Twist Grill and coffee shop.

$$ **COLUMBIA HOTEL**
95 Lancaster Gate
Tel: 402 0021
Telex: 21879
This Victorian hotel overlooks Hyde Park and, if you are lucky, you can get a room with a view of the park. 90 of the 93 rooms have bath/shower. All rooms have phone and television.

$ **ELYSEE**
25 Craven Terrace
Tel: 402 7633
Small economy hotel close to Hyde Park. Restaurant, bar and disco.

$$ **PLAZA HOTEL**
42 Princes Square
Tel: 229 1292
Large tourist-class hotel located near Bayswater underground station. Close to Portobello Road. All rooms have been redecorated and have private bathroom. Restaurant and bar.

$$ **ROYAL EAGLE**
26 Craven Road
Tel: 723 3262
Telex: 24939
Budget hotel convenient to Paddington Station and Lancaster Gate underground station. Basic but clean rooms with private bathroom and color T.V.

$ **STRUTTON PARK HOTEL**
45 Palace Court
Tel: 727 5074
Telex: 896559 GECOMS G Attn. Strutton Park
Victorian building close to Portobello Road. Most rooms with shower. Restaurant and bar.

$ **WESTPOINT HOTEL**
170 Sussex Gardens
Tel: 402 0281
This budget priced hotel is close to Hyde Park and the West End.

W.8. Hotels

$$ **KENSINGTON CLOSE HOTEL**
Wrights Lane
Tel: 937 8170
Telex: 23914
This large distinguished hotel has an indoor heated swimming pool, squash courts, sauna and mini gym. All 530 rooms have private bathroom, color T.V. and telephone.

$$ **KENSINGTON PALACE HOTEL**
De Vere Gardens
Tel: 937 8121 U.S. 800 847 4358
Telex: 262422
Overlooking Kensington Gardens and close to the Albert Hall. Within walking distance of the many specialist antique shops in Kensington Church Street. 298 rooms all with private bathroom, T.V. and telephone. Restaurant, cocktail bar, lounge bar and coffee shop.

W.8.

$$$$ **ROYAL GARDEN HOTEL**
Kensington High Street
Tel: 937 8000
Telex: 263151
Luxury hotel on the edge of Kensington Gardens and Hyde Park. 411 rooms all with private bath, shower, color T.V. and mini-bar. Three restaurants, lounge and bars.

W.9. Hotels

$$ **COLONNADE HOTEL**
2 Warrington Crescent
Tel: 289 2167
Telex: 298930
Small comfortable Georgian hotel. Most rooms with bath or shower. Restaurant and bar.

W.C.1. Hotels

$$ **PRESIDENT HOTEL**
Russell Square
Tel: 837 8844
Telex: 263951
This well-kept hotel has 450 rooms all with bath/shower, phone and television with in-house movies. Lounge, bar and coffee shop.

$$$ **RUSSELL HOTEL**
Russel Square
Tel: 837 6470
Telex: 24615
This traditional first-class hotel of late Victorian architecture is located between the City and the West End. 318 rooms all with color T.V., direct-dial telephone and mini-bar. Restaurant, grill room, bar and lounge area.

$$ **TAVISTOCK HOTEL**
Tavistock Square
Tel: 636 8383
The proprietors of the President Hotel also run this large hotel. 301 rooms each with bath/shower, phone and television with in-house movies. Two bars and comfortable lounge.

W.C.2. Hotels

$$ **THE MOUNTBATTEN**
Seven Dials
Covent Garden
Tel: 836 4300 U.S. 800 447 7011
Telex: 298087
Small luxury hotel opened in August 1985. 127 attractive bedrooms with bathroom, telephone, hairdryer and double glazing. Satellite television to link up with U.S. channels.

$$$$ **THE SAVOY**
Strand
Tel: 836 4343 U.S. 800 223 6800 (N.Y. State-call collect 212 838 3110)
Telex: 24234
Opened in 1889, this lovely hotel is elegantly furnished with antiques and has views of the River Thames, Houses of Parliament and City of London. Excellent restaurants, shopping arcade and a Keith Prowse theater ticket agency.

S.W.1. Hotels

$ **ANNANDALE HOUSE HOTEL**
39 Sloane Gardens
Tel: 730 5051
Charming Victorian house near Sloane Square. Most rooms with shower or bath.

$$$$ **CADOGAN THISTLE**
75 Sloane Street
Tel: 235 7141 U.S. 800 847 4358
Telex: 267893
Located in fashionable Chelsea, this 19th cent. style hotel has all the 20th cent. comforts. 69 rooms all with private bathrooms.

$$ **DOLPHIN SQUARE**
Dolphin Square
Tel: 834 9134
This may well be the answer to the person who wants to feel at home! Rent a furnished apartment by the day, the week or the month. Discounts usually given for stays of a week or more. Facilities include a shopping arcade, restaurant open from 7.30am until midnight, two bars, Finnish log saunas, heated indoor swimming pool, squash courts, travel and theater agency, large underground garage and lovely gardens. Each apartment is completely furnished, has a private bathroom, fully equipped kitchen, radio and color T.V. Free maid service 6 days a week. Rates are really reasonable.

$ **ELIZABETH HOTEL**
37 Eccleston Square
Tel: 828 6812
Friendly, quiet hotel close to Victorian Station. 24 rooms, three of which have shower and television.

$ **GEORGIAN HOUSE HOTEL**
35 St. George's Drive
Tel: 834 1438
Family owned bed & breakfast hotel within walking distance of Victoria Station. Most rooms with shower or bath.

$$$$ **THE LOWNDES THISTLE HOTEL**
21 Lowndes Street
Tel: 235 6020 U.S. 800 847 4358
Telex: 919065
This quiet elegant hotel is close to Knightsbridge and Harrods. 80 rooms all with private bathrooms, color T.V. and telephone.

S.W.1.

$$$ **ROYAL HORSEGUARDS**
2 Whitehall Court
Tel: 839 3400 U.S. 800 847 4358
Telex: 917096
This 284 room hotel overlooks the Thames and the Royal Festival Hall.

S.W.3. Hotels

$$$ **BASIL STREET HOTEL**
8 Basil Street, Knightsbridge
Tel: 581 3311
Telex: 28379
This charming hotel is located behind Harrods. Known for its high standard of service and attractive decor, this long established first class hotel offers every comfort and is immaculately kept. 68 of the 96 rooms have bath/shower, all rooms have telephone and television. Excellent dining offering traditional dishes.

$$$$ **CAPITAL**
22-24 Basil Street
Tel: 589 5171
Telex: 919042
Within walking distance of Harrods, this recently refurbished hotel has a very fine restaurant and bar.
60 rooms.

$$ **THE CLAVERLEY**
13-14 Beaufort Gardens
Tel: 589 8541
Privately owned hotel around the corner from Harrods. Most rooms with private bath.

$$$ **L'HOTEL**
28 Basil Street
Tel: 589 6286
Telex: 919042
Attractively decorated, this small hotel is under the same management as the Capital. No restaurant but splendid wine bar downstairs with snacks available and excellent restaurant at the Capital next door. 12 rooms with bath/shower, phone and television.

S.W.5. Hotels

$$ **BURNS HOTEL**
18-26 Barkston Gardens
Tel: 373 3151
Telex: 27885
104 room hotel near Earl's Court. Good food.

$$+ **LONDON INTERNATIONAL HOTEL**
147 Cromwell Road
Tel: 370 4200
Telex: 27260
This large modern hotel is close to the South Kensington museums. 417 rooms, each with bath/shower, telephone and television with in-house movies.

$$ **ADELPHI HOTEL**
127 Cromwell Road
Tel: 373 7177
Telex: 8813164
Well-kept comfortable hotel with lounge, bar and breakfast room. 52 rooms all with bath/shower, telephone and television with in-house movies.

$ **CRANLEY PLACE HOTEL**
One Cranley Place
Tel: 589 7944
Large elegant rooms and attractive decor in the Laura Ashley style. Convenient for visiting those antique furniture dealers in the Fulham Road area. Also close to South Kensington underground station.

$$ **THE EDWARDIAN HOTEL**
40 Harrington Gardens
Tel: 370 4444
This charming hotel is situated in a pleasant and quiet area of Kensington. All rooms have private bath or shower and include color T.V., radio and telephone. Dining room and bar.

$$ **NUMBER SIXTEEN**
16 Sumner Place
Tel: 589 5232
Telex: 266638
The antiques and beautiful floral arrangements decorating this Victorian hotel provide a comfortable atmosphere. 32 rooms, 30 of which have bath/shower, all rooms have telephone and television.

$$$ **REMBRANDT HOTEL**
11 Thurloe Place
Tel: 589 8100
Telex: 295828
Popular hotel close to South Kensington underground station and within walking distance of Harrods. 200 rooms, each with bath/shower, telephone and television. Indoor swimming pool, gymnasium, sauna andd solarium.

$$ **THE VANDERBILT**
76-86 Cromwell Road
Tel: 589 2424 U.S. 800 447 7011
Telex: 919867
Elegant Victorian-style hotel in Kensington. Walk to Gloucester Road underground station. 230 rooms all with private bath/shower, color T.V., in-room video films and direct-dial telephone. The Marlborough Room restaurant is excellent.

Where to dine

London is a richly cosmopolitan city and this is shown in the diversity of restaurants, some of which are shown in this section. Price categories are denoted by the number of $'s and signify the average cost of a meal for one person, inclusive of V.A.T.

$	under $12	$$$	$25-$50
$$	$12-$25	$$$$	over $50

W.1. Restaurants

$$ **AUNTIES**
126 Cleveland Street
Tel: 387 3226
Victorian-style restaurant featuring good English home cooking. Closed Sunday.

$$$ **BENTLEY'S OYSTER BAR**
11-15 Swallow Street
Tel: 734 0401 (Oyster Bar)
734 4756 (Restaurant)
Old, established seafood restaurant upstairs, oyster bar on the ground floor. Closed Sunday.

$ **BUNCH OF GRAPES**
16 Shepherd Market
Tel: 629 4989
Victorian pub decorated with antiques. Carvery downstairs, hot and cold buffet available in the upstairs restaurant.

$ **CHICAGO PIZZA PIE FACTORY**
17 Hanover Square
Tel: 629 2669
For that American deep-dish pizza you can't live without! U.S. football videos shown. Take-out.

$$$$ **DORCHESTER GRILL**
Park Lane
Tel: 629 8888
Excellent service and beautiful surroundings enhance the consistently fine cuisine.

$$$$ **LE GAVROCHE**
43 Upper Brook Street
Tel: 408 0881
One of the outstanding French restaurants in London. Expensive, but worth it!

$$$ **THE GREENHOUSE**
27a Hay's Mews
Tel: 499 3331
Friendly Anglo-French restaurant in the center of Mayfair. Light atmosphere and efficient service - try the lemon syllabub for dessert. Closed Sunday.

$$ **LITTLE AKROPOLIS**
10 Charlotte Street
Tel: 636 8198
Charming Greek restaurant offering carefully prepared specialities. Excellent moussaka and rose petal pancakes.

$$$ **MARQUIS**
121a Mount Street
Tel: 499 1256
Elegant Mayfair restaurant offering a choice of French and Italian dishes.

$$ **MAYFLOWER**
68-70 Shaftesbury Avenue
Tel: 734 9207
Popular Cantonese restaurant in theaterland. Open until 3.30am.

$$$ **TANG DYNASTY**
19 New Cavendish Street
Tel: 935 3570
This new Chinese restaurant is run by the established Mr. Kai of Mayfair. Although the food is less expensive than the South Audley St. establishment, it is every bit as appetizing.

$$ **TIDDY DOLLS**
2 Hertford Street
Tel: 499 2357
Named after an 18th century ginger-breadmaker, this restaurant is located in Shepherd Market and features traditional English food. Rather touristy, but fun.

W.2. Restaurants

$$ **KHYBER**
56 Westbourne Grove
Tel: 727 4385
Pleasant Indian restaurant offering a wide range of tandoori, seafood and great curries. Take-out.

$ **THE RAJ**
57 Westbourne Grove
Tel: 229 2551
Attractive restaurant, close to Portobello, serving very reasonably priced Indian food.

W.6. Restaurants

$ **QUEEN'S HEAD**
Brook Green
Tel: 603 3174
300 year old inn with beer garden in the rear and public tennis courts at the front. Typical English fare includes roast beef and steak & kidney pie.

W.8. Restaurants

$ **CHURCHILL ARMS**
119 Kensington Church Street
Tel: 727 4242
Attractive Fullers pub with beer garden in the rear.

$$ **MAGGIE JONES**
6 Old Court Place, Kensington Church St.
Tel: 937 6462
English home-style cooking in a country-kitchen atmosphere.

$ **MILDRED'S**
135 Kensington Church Street
Tel: 727 5452
Anglo-French menu features chicken & mushroom pie, quiches, steak, chocolate mousse and apple tart. Closed Saturday & Sunday.

$$ **TWIN BROTHERS**
51 Kensington Church Street
Tel: 937 4152
Small, cozy restaurant serving authentic German specialities including schnitzel, fish dishes and chicken Kiev.

$ **THE WINDSOR CASTLE**
114 Campden Hill Road
Tel: 727 8491
Small busy pub serving good bar food.

W.11. Restaurants

$ **SUN IN SPLENDOUR**
7 Portobello Road
Tel: 727 6345
Small attractive pub offering excellent home-cooked food.

S.W.1. Restaurants

$$$ **CARLTON TOWER RIB ROOM**
Cadogan Place
Tel: 235 5411
Smart restaurant known for the excellence of it's roast beef. 'Happy hour' from 5.30-7pm.

$$$ **MR CHOW**
151 Knightsbridge
Tel 589 7347
Established Chinese restaurant in fashionable Knightsbridge. Reservation advised.

$$$ **GRENADIER**
18 Wilton Row
Tel: 235 3074
Said to have been the Duke of Wellington's 'local'. The ceiling is covered with wine labels in this mews pub. Try their Beef Wellington.

S.W.1. Restaurants

$$$$ **MAXIM'S DE PARIS**
32 Panton Street
Tel: 839 4809
Pierre Cardin and Kennedy Brookes combined to recreate the Parisian legend in the heart of London. Excellent French food and wine list. Closed Sunday.

$ **SMILES**
16-17 Jermyn Street
Tel: 734 7334
Anglo-American menu: burgers, chili, bangers & mash and great desserts.

S.W.3. Restaurants

$ **ADMIRAL CODRINGTON**
17 Mossop Street
Tel: 589 4603
Victorian-style pub decorated with antiques, serving curries, steak & kidney pie, steaks, salads and homemade pies for dessert.

$$$$ **CAPITAL HOTEL**
22 Basil Street, Knightsbridge
Tel: 589 5171
Excellent French cuisine in an elegant atmosphere.

$$$ **ENGLISH HOUSE**
3 Milner Street, Chelsea
Tel: 584 3002
18th century English cooking at it's best.

$ **LA GARIBALDINA**
390 King's Road, Chelsea
Tel: 351 1896
Inexpensive Italian restaurant serving excellent pasta and delicious desserts. Closed Sunday.

$$$ **PARKES**
5 Beauchamp Place
Tel: 589 1390
Small, sophisticated restaurant featuring beautifully presented Anglo-French dishes.

$$$$ **LA TANTE CLAIR**
68 Royal Hospital Road
Tel: 352 6045
Very fine French cuisine, delectable desserts. Fine wine list. Closed Saturday & Sunday.

S.W.6. Restaurants

$$$ **GASTRONOME ONE**
311 New King's Road
Tel: 731 6381
Excellent French restaurant, good wine list. Don't be put off by the entrance, if you like French food — this is a 'must'.

S.W.6.

$ **THE WHITE HORSE**
1 Parson's Green
Tel: 736 2115
Victorian-style pub and wine bar. Jazz is featured on Thursday evenings. Excellent homemade food.

S.W.10. Restaurants

$$ **HUNGRY HORSE**
196 Fulham Road
Tel: 352 7757
Traditional English cooking featuring boiled beef & dumplings, kedgeree and treacle tart. Closed Sunday.

S.E.10. Restaurants

$$ **CUTTY SARK**
Ballast Quay, Lassell Street
Tel: 858 3146
Georgian pub overlooking the River Thames. English traditional food.

$$ **LE PAPILLON**
57 Greenwich Church Street
Tel: 858 2668
Intimate French dining opposite the 'Cutty Sark'. Closed Sunday.

$$ **TRAFALGAR TAVERN**
Park Row
Tel: 858 2437
Fully restored historical pub originally built in 1837, overlooks the river. English fare.

S.E.16. Restaurants

$$ **MAYFLOWER**
117 Rotherhithe Street
Tel: 237 4088
A 17th Century riverside pub serving hot and cold food of excellent value.

E.1. Restaurants

$$ **BLOOM'S**
90 Whitechapel High Street
Tel: 247 6001
Busy kosher restaurant - eat here on Sunday after visiting Cutler Street Market. Take-out. Closed Saturday.

E.14. Restaurants

$$ **GOOD FRIENDS**
139 Salmon Lane
Tel: 987 5541
Basic Chinese restaurant in tough Limehouse district, features Cantonese dishes at reasonable prices.

E.C.3. Restaurants

$$ **GEORGE & VULTURE**
3 Castle Court
Tel: 626 9710
This 12th century pub was Pickwick's London headquarters and is reputed to be haunted. Charles Dickens was also a regular. English traditional fare - closed Sat. & Sun.

E.C.4. Restaurants

$$ **YE OLDE CHESHIRE CHEESE**
145 Fleet Street
Tel: 353 6170
Famous old inn offers English specialities including steak & kidney pie and roast beef.

$$ **PRINTERS PIE**
60 Fleet Street
Tel: 353 8861
Typical English pub menu in a pleasant atmosphere.

W.C.2. Restaurants

$ **FOOD FOR THOUGHT**
31 Neal Street, Covent Garden
Tel: 836 0239
Inexpensive, tiny restaurant serving imaginative vegetarian dishes. Very busy at lunchtime. Closed Saturday & Sunday.

$ **ROCK SOLE PLAICE**
47 Endell Street
Tel: 836 3785
Inexpensive fish restaurant in the Covent Garden area. Fresh fish, pies and sausages. Fast and efficient service.

$$$ **RULES**
35 Maiden Lane, Strand
Tel: 836 5314
This well-known eating establishment boasts some very distinguished customers, namely Edward VII and Charles Dickens. English dishes served in this gracious atmosphere include jugged hare, boiled beef & dumplings and braised oxtail. Closed Sunday.

W.C.2.

$$$$ **SAVOY GRILL ROOM**
Savoy Hotel
Strand
Tel: 836 4343
Famous restaurant in world famous hotel. First-rate food and perfect service in a dignified atmosphere. Closed Sunday.

$$ **SHERLOCK HOLMES**
10 Northumberland Street
Tel: 930 2644
A must for fans of the great sleuth. Holmes' Baker Street study is reconstructed upstairs in this interesting pub. Anglo-French menu.

$$$ **SIMPSONS IN THE STRAND**
100 Strand
Tel: 836 9112
Around the corner from the Savoy, this distinguished restaurant is known for the excellence of it's meat. Men's bar in cellar. Reservations essential. Closed Sunday.

N.1. Restaurants

$$$ **FREDERICK'S**
Camden Passage
Tel: 359 2888
A patio garden and conservatory enhance the ambiance of this popular restaurant. Large varied menu. Reservations recommended. Closed Sunday.

$$ **M'SIEUR FROG**
31a Essex Road, Islington
Tel: 226 3495
Warm, friendly atmosphere in this bistro near Camden Passage. Popular with local residents, this charming restaurant offers high quality food mainly with a flavor of Northern France.

$$ **RISTORANTE PORTOFINO**
39 Camden Passage
Tel: 226 1479
Popular Italian restaurant in the heart of 'antique city'. Closed Sunday.

$ **SERENDIPITY**
The Mall, Camden Passage
Tel: 359 1932
Light, summery atmosphere in this restaurant/wine bar above the antique shops in the Mall. Casseroles are good value. Service is attentive. Good Sunday Brunch.

$ **UPPER STREET FISH SHOP**
324 Upper Street
Tel: 359 1401
If you wish to try the popular British fish'n'chips, this is one of the best fish shops in town. Friendly bistro atmosphere and wide selection of fish offered. Take-out. Closed Sunday.

British Royal Commemoratives

by Audrey B. Zeder

After an overview of royal commemorative history, individual members of British royalty (and the commemoratives they inspired) are singled out. Included are Queen Victoria, Edward VII, George V, Edward VIII, George VI, Elizabeth II and Prince Charles/Princess Diana and their children. More than 200 photographs, many in color, illustrate the various forms commemoratives can take — ceramics, tins, silver and ephemeral of every description. This is an excellent guide to a fascinating collecting hobby that can be actively pursued with a large or small budget. Published by Wallace Homestead Book Co., 8½ x 11 Softbound. Available in selected book stores or copies may be ordered directly from the author.

To order your copy:

Send your name, address and phone number along with a check or money order for $17. 95 plus $2 postage/handling (Calif. residents add 6% sales tax) to:

AUDREY B. ZEDER
6755 CORALITE [P]
LONG BEACH, CA 90808

USEFUL ADDRESSES

British Tourist Authority

40 West 57th Street, New York, NY 10019 ....Tel: (212) 581 4700

John Hancock Center, Suite 3320,
875 North Michigan Avenue, Chicago, IL 60611.........Tel: (312) 787 0490

612 South Flower Street, Los Angeles, CA 90017 ....Tel: (213) 623 8196

Cedar Maple Plaza
2305 Cedar Springs, Dallas, TX 75201................Tel: (214) 720 4040

British Travel Centre
4 Lower Regent Street, London S.W.1.......................Tel: 01 730 3400

American Express
6 Haymarket, S.W.1.................................Tel: 01 930 4411

American Chamber of Commerce
75 Brook Street, London W.1.........................Tel: 01 493 0381

U.S. Embassy
24 Grosvenor Square, London W.1. ....Tel: 01 499 9000

Post Office - open 24 hrs.
24 William IV Street, Trafalgar Square, W.C.2. ....Tel: 01 930 9580

International Telephone and Telex Bureau
1a The Broadway, St. James's, S.W.1. ....Tel: 01 222 6155

Avis
35 Headfort Place, Belgravia, London S.W.1. ....Tel: 01 245 9862
....U.S. 800 331 1084

Hertz
35 Edgware Road, London W.2.........................Tel: 01 402 4242
....U.S. 800 654 3001

London and Provincial Antique Dealers Association
3 Cheval Place, London SW7 1EW ....Tel: 01 584 7911

British Antique Dealers Association
20 Rutland Gate, London SW7 1BD......................Tel: 01 589 4128

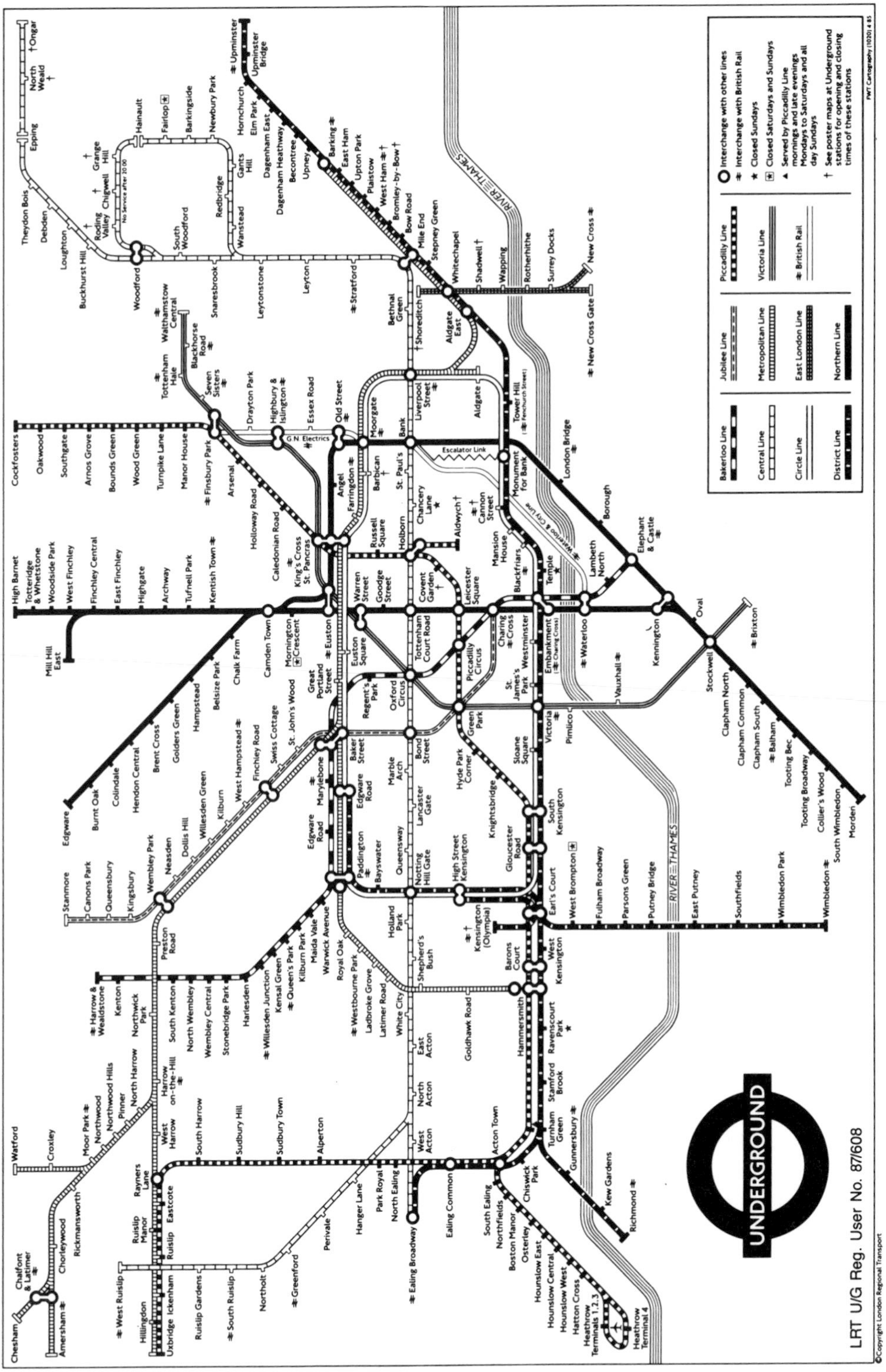
Bakerloo Line
Central Line
Circle Line
District Line
Jubilee Line
Metropolitan Line
East London Line
Northern Line
Piccadilly Line
Victoria Line
British Rail
Interchange with other lines
Interchange with British Rail
Closed Sundays
Closed Saturdays and Sundays
Served by Piccadilly Line mornings and late evenings Mondays to Saturdays and all day Sundays
See poster maps at Underground stations for opening and closing times of these stations
FWT Cartography (1020) 4 85
UNDERGROUND
LRT U/G Reg. User No. 87/608
©Copyright London Regional Transport